GENERATIVE
TOUCH

John Parmater

GENERATIVE
TOUCH

A new way to heal

GREAT
WORKS
press

Generative Touch: A New Way to Heal

Library of Congress Catalog Card Number 95-95344

Parmater, John Q.
Generative Touch: A New Way to Heal / John Q. Parmater
ISBN 0-9649422-0-8

To my parents

Harold and Helen Parmater

...and then the day came

when the risk to

remain tight in a bud

was more painful

than the risk

it took to blossom.

ANAIS NIN

Contents

SECTION ONE

A healing system

SECTION TWO

Watch the healing happen!

SECTION THREE

How to heal

SECTION FOUR

Finding fulfillment through healing

A healing system

Chapter One

Beginnings

I didn't set out to heal people with touch. Actually, it started with a lucky accident. While sitting in the back row of a seminar I put my hands on the shoulders of my friend Pat Baker. Pretty soon she turned to me and said, "John, you have healing hands."

That got my mind going on the effects of touch. What are healing hands? Is there such a thing? Do I have them? To find out, I did some experiments. A guy in a seminar was slouched over looking really tired, so I put my hands on his upper back for a few minutes. He straightened up and looked more alert. A woman in a training had a stiff neck. I put my hands on her neck, her body tingled a little bit, and the stiffness went away.

I didn't know what it was, but I was on to something. Next, I was fortunate enough to get a client who had severe problems with pain. She had been in a car wreck when she was 11. At age 40, she still had so much pain she could hardly ride in a car. She wore an electrical device that pumped voltage through electrodes attached to her body, trying to block the pain. As she sat in my office, her pain was so intense that every time she shifted her position in the chair, she turned the knobs of her electrical device to adjust the voltage. She had knots in her back from the tension and the pain. Every week, she got a massage to soften the knots, but they always came back.

I put my hands on her and the knots softened. By the end of the session, she had unplugged her electrical device. I asked what happened and she said the pain was gone—she didn't need it any more. When she went back to her massage therapist, the knots were still gone. She doesn't even need massages any more. And now she rides comfortably in the car.

By now you're probably saying, "Okay, so you're a healer. What's that got to do with me?" Here's what it's got to do with you: You can become a healer, too. You can heal yourself and others. This book will show you how. It's easy, it's fast, and actually, it's a lot of fun. But before I tell you how to do it, let me tell you some more about what you can do with it.

You can also heal emotional issues with touch. One of my clients was forced (by her mother) to have a nose job (rhinoplasty is the medical term) when she was fourteen. She had been upset about it ever since, and was still mad at her mother after all these years. We healed her anger and resentment in less than an hour. Then she went home and cured her daughter's nightmares. This eight-year-old girl was waking up every night, screaming her head off. She had been doing this since she was two. Pretty hard on the mother and the daughter. So the next few nights when her daughter woke up, she put her hand on the part of the body where the girl felt the fear. After three nights of this her daughter started sleeping peacefully. And she still does.

It works on physical abuse, too. One of my clients needed his legs and buttocks healed from whippings he received as a child. Another needed his face healed from slaps he got from his mother and father.

A friend of mine had a character trait he didn't like and he asked me if we could heal it. He was a speaker and he would get arrogant with his audiences. When I put my hands on him, he saw a picture of a bully—the kid who used to beat him up in the fifth grade. As the healing took place, the bully picture got small and far away. My client said, "Oh, he's just a little kid. I don't need to fight him any more." End of arrogance.

I've used this process with more issues than I can remember. I'm amazed at what it does. Almost anyone can heal people by placing their hands on them in the way described in this book. Couples are already using it to help each other with emotional issues and physical symptoms. Parents are using it to heal the emotional wounds of their children. It can be used with traditional healing arts. Practitioners of body work are extending and enhancing their results by adding this method of healing to their repertoire.

The amazing thing about this healing method is how well it lasts. Once the person is healed, he or she stays healed. The clients I just mentioned got their healings several years ago and they are still healed.

This is a powerful and effective healing tool that is easy to learn and easy to do. It's completely safe and reliable. I have used it hundreds of times on issues as diverse as anger, frustration, resentment, guilt, confusion, fear, trauma, abuse, abandonment, grief and more. I have also used it with sprained ankles, headaches, neck aches, backaches, and pre-menstrual syndrome. When used through time, it leads to core emotional healing and a profound sense of well-being.

From an accidental beginning in 1988 with Pat Baker, this approach to healing has developed into a mature and consistent way to heal yourself and others and find your path to health and fulfillment. I am grateful for the opportunity to share it with you.

Chapter Two

Parts

"Wearing dark glasses at night! Running red lights! How many lights did I run? Seven? Nine? Wow—I almost hit that car! What is wrong with me? What am I doing? Racing through the streets of Detroit at 90 miles an hour! I've got to get help."

Gus had a compulsion to drive recklessly in the city. And although he hated to admit he couldn't solve the problem himself—and though he thought therapists were kind of weird—Gus found a therapist.

Gus: "Doc! I find myself riding my motorcycle late at night—at high speeds—on dark streets—in populated areas. If somebody opened a car door or a dog ran out in front of me, I could be killed—in an instant! It's like... some part of me... takes over and... makes me do it. I'm out of control. I can't keep from doin' it."

Therapist: "Ask the part of you that makes you do this behavior—ask it what it wants."

(Gus was so desperate that he was willing to play along with the therapist, pretending he had parts, even though the whole idea seemed very strange to him. But he'd done strange things before. So he went ahead and asked the part, and surprisingly enough, the part answered him.)

Gus: "The part says it wants to kill me!"

Therapist: "Thank the part, because we know all parts want good things for us. Sometimes they just go about it in the wrong way. Parts are like people. Sometimes they set out to do a good thing, but they mess it up.

(Gus sighed heavily and thanked the part, but quite reluctantly.)

"Now ask that part, 'And if you kill Gus, what will that do for him that's even more important?'"

Gus: "The part says it wants to put me out of my misery."

Therapist: "Oh, okay, the part wants to put you out of your misery. Thank the part and ask it, "If you're out of your misery, what will that do for you ?"

Gus: "The part says my life is such a mess that if it puts me out of my misery, I'll feel better."

Therapist: "Oh, so the part wants you to feel better. Great! Now ask the part, 'If there were a way that you could help Gus feel better without killing him—another way that would work at least as well—would you be willing to consider it?'"

Gus: "The part says, 'Yes, of course. If there is a way that will work at least as well, I'll take it.'"

The therapist helped the part find more ways to help Gus feel better. Immediately after the session, Gus stopped his outrageous behavior and he soon found himself doing things to make him feel better and be happy. With new choices, Gus's part was willing and able to guide his life in new directions.

Gus had been driven to dangerous behavior by a misguided part that wanted something good for him; it wanted to stop the pain. But it didn't know how. Gus later revealed that he had also been getting into fights and drinking excessively. Gus soon found himself "spontaneously" doing good things for himself.

Six months later he sold the motorcycle.

I assume all parts have positive intentions. But parts sometimes communicate by getting us to do outrageous behaviors. Gus's part was making him do something that could have killed him—even though it only wanted to help! So the therapist offered the part the chance to find new ways to help, and the part accepted his offer. In my work with clients over the years, I have found that parts doggedly pursue their goals; if you offer them a better way to do what they already want to do, they almost always say yes. When Gus's part accepted the therapist's help and got new choices, his behavior changed for the better.

Parts—What Are They?

You can think of a part as a section of your mind that is responsible for a specific behavior or feeling. Some parts create behaviors that cause us trouble. These parts need to know about new choices. Like Gus's part that ultimately wanted him to be happy, some parts, even with positive intention, get us to do behaviors that can hurt us. These parts are like frightened little children who have lost their parents and are doing the best they can to survive in a world that seems hostile and cold. To protect themselves, these parts put up walls—walls which separate them—walls that keep them alone.

Resourceful and Unresourceful Parts

Not all parts are troubled. Some parts are very capable. Have you ever driven home from the store when you had so much on your mind that you didn't remember the drive at all? While you were thinking about your job, your kids and your money, who was driving the car? Your "driving" part. It steps on the gas pedal, maintains speed, turns corners, and watches for stop signs. It's a very resourceful part.

We all have many facets to our personalities. Most facets represent positive qualities. For example, many people probably have a cheerful side, a serious side, an intense side, and so forth. It is obvious that people have parts that make them extremely happy and spur them to outstanding achievements, parts that persevere in the face of discouragement or danger, and parts that display grace, love and kindness. The many facets of our personalities make us interesting and competent.

People we encounter bring out various parts of us. A friend may bring out our caring part. A boss could bring out our punctual part. A parent might bring out a childish part.

Do you have a part that makes you do high quality work? Or a part that helps you develop rich and satisfying relationships? Our resourceful parts guide us in making fulfilling life choices and relating to people. They remember how to hit a tennis ball or perform long division. They also take care of functions like heartbeat, breathing, digestion, and other body processes.

But some less fortunate parts seem to have fewer resources available to them. They may feel angry, ashamed, worthless, embarrassed or depressed. Or they may make us sabotage relationships or eat too many hot fudge sundaes.

And sometimes our parts (and our behaviors) are in conflict. One part wants to take bold action, but another part is afraid to move. One part wants you to ask for a raise, but another part says, "No." One part wants the cheesecake but another part wants you to watch your weight.

Even if you go ahead and do what one part wants, another part may keep pestering you about what it wants. When you're working, do you ever have a part that wants to play? When you're playing, do you ever have a part that wants you to work? When you're eating a delicious dessert, does a part of you feel guilty and try to get you to stop?

With so many resources inside us, how is it possible that some parts can be so devoid of resources? It's as if some parts somehow lose touch with our inner wisdom. They get separated from our inner selves and try to survive on their own.

Splitting to Accommodate Another Point of View

Parts can split off when the words the child hears from an authority figure do not match what he sees, hears and feels in the real world. For example, suppose Daddy is drunk and passed out on the kitchen floor. Mother says "Daddy's just tired," and the child knows that she's supposed to say, "Yes, Daddy's just tired." A part of the child knows the truth, sees Daddy, and knows Daddy is drunk. But to please her mother, the child mentally steps out of herself and creates a new part that says, "Yes, Daddy's just tired."

Before a child has reached certain developmental stages, she takes in whatever her mother says as "true." Yet, what she sees with her eyes is also "true." She doesn't have the mental skill to represent her mother's words as simply another person's model of the world. So the two parts allow for both "truths": the "truth" presented by her mother and the "truth" she sees. Each part knows only its own "truth." The new part will be less resourceful than the original part because it was created only to accommodate Mother's point of view—it is less connected to the child's overall reality. But the new part may be the one presented to the outside world more often because it is validated by her mother. In later life, this part may strongly defend its version of the truth—Daddy's just tired—even if Mother is out of the picture.

It can get even worse. If the child is molested by Daddy at night, but during the day, Mother says, "Daddy loves you. You love him don't you?" then the child may separate into two parts: one that knows what happens at night and another that agrees with Mother. Since the "good Daddy" is the model that is validated in the outside world, she will probably keep the "abuser Daddy" out of memory and only be conscious of the "good Daddy."

On a lesser scale, suppose the child gets angry and mother says, "You don't really feel that way," or "Don't be angry." Again, the child separates, creating a new part that "doesn't feel that way." Now there are two parts: One that is angry and one that "doesn't feel that way." This is how we learn not to feel our feelings.

But it doesn't have to be that way. If Mother or Father would say, "Oh, it looks like you're angry. Do you want to tell me about it? How can I help you?" then there would be no need for us to split into parts.

Anger is only one of many feelings that can be repressed. If I've been taught that my feelings are not okay, I may habitually make parts that help me repress them. It happens this way: I feel fear; I believe I shouldn't feel fear, so I step out of it. Then I don't feel the fear. I have created a new part that doesn't feel the fear. Another example: I'm really annoyed at someone. Well, I shouldn't be. So I separate from myself. I submerge the annoyed part and attend to the part that is not annoyed.

By repeating this process, we can end up with many dissociated parts. Some social systems and some religions support this separation by teaching us that parts of us are not okay.

We are inclined to forget about or repress parts that are "not okay." Repressed parts often express themselves indirectly or sporadically. They may create smoldering anger or outbursts of rage. Research relating unexpressed emotions to physical ailments hints that repressed parts may be responsible for backaches, headaches, stomach upset, ulcers, high blood pressure, and perhaps even cancer and auto-immune disease. An angry part that wants to hurt or attack another person, but is held in check by a socially responsible part, may become confused and begin to attack one's own body.

Splitting During Traumatic Events

Parts can be formed during significant emotional events. Al, an auto worker, had a fear of approaching people, fear of authority figures, and an overwhelming fear of adult males. When we traced his fear back to childhood, Al remembered his father plowing fields with a huge tractor. Al ran to greet his father, who didn't see him at first and nearly ran over him. His father was so angry and upset that he jumped down from the tractor and beat up Al, who was only three years old. After that traumatic experience, Al had parts that loved his father and other parts that were afraid of him.

Rex, a business executive, had a fear of asking for what he wanted. When we traced that feeling back in time to the first time he ever felt it, Rex suddenly remembered his father saying, "NO." Rex was two, and he asked his dad to read the comics to him. Prior to this time, Rex's dad had always said "Yes" to such requests. This time he said, "NO." Rex was frightened and formed a part that feared his dad. Rex's symptom in later life was a fear of asking for things.

Paula, a court reporter, sometimes felt helpless in getting people to understand her. When we traced that feeling back in time, Paula remembered that when she was three, her 13-year-old cousin got on top of her and molested her. She broke free and went crying to her parents, but they did not understand what she was crying about. As an adult, Paula had forgotten the incident, but she still felt helpless.

Each of these events formed a part with beliefs and feelings that continued to limit the person's choices throughout childhood and all the way into adulthood. In circumstances that the part interpreted as similar to the original incident, the part would become unresourceful and regress the person into the feelings from childhood. All that was needed was an event to trigger the old feeling.

Splitting to Define a New Reality

New parts can appear when pleasing others is more important than accepting reality. The two parts can allow two "truths" to co-exist.

Bob's father didn't keep a regular job. His father was ashamed and Bob felt that shame. But the family wanted Bob to be proud of his father, so Bob split into two parts: one proud and one ashamed.

Taking Others Inside

We can also create parts by taking other people inside us. Each of us is probably familiar with a part that represents our mother, for example, and another part that represents our father. These "people" parts may carry with them not only our parents' wisdom, but also their pain, which needs to be healed.

Mixed Messages and Parts

When a person sends a mixed message, we sometimes deal with the two parts of the message by recruiting two parts to receive them. Here's an example. One day I was having lunch with some friends and I was wearing my ring. Cynthia looked at me and said, "I really like your ring," while shaking her head side to side as if to say, "No." I recognized her intended mixed message and smiled at her. Then someone else at the table said, "John, you covered up your ring." I looked down to see the fingers of my left hand covering the ring on my right hand.

I didn't even realize what I had done!

Two parts of me responded to Cynthia's statement; one part saw her shaking her head and listened to the words, "I really like your ring," while another part got the message expressed by shaking her head, which was, "I don't like your ring." That part (which was out of my awareness) got me to cover up my ring. So, I had two parts going; one was paying attention to the words and movements and another was feeling ashamed.

I was aware of only one of the parts: the part that heard her words and saw her shaking her head. The part of me that covered up my ring was out of my awareness. It was probably frightened or shamed in response to Cynthia's shaking her head, so it covered the ring to hide from her apparent disapproval.

When a child is forming his personality, he can create parts in response to mixed messages. As an adult, those same parts are ready to respond to new mixed messages. He can split at the slightest confusion.

How Parts Communicate with Us

Parts communicate through thoughts, emotions, behaviors, and body sensations. A happy part may give me tears of joy. My shamed part got me to cover up my ring. An afraid part may increase heart rate or blood pressure. An embarrassed part may cause your face to get red. A stressed part may create a backache or headache. A guilty part may cause a knot in your stomach. If you don't respond to those signals, the part may communicate by causing pain. And if you don't respond to the pain, the part may take further steps, like body degeneration or disease.

Occasionally when we are working with physical symptoms such as headaches or backaches, the part will increase the intensity of the pain. This signal lets us know we have the part's attention.

Communicating with Parts through Touch

After talking with parts for a few years, much like the therapist who talked with Gus's parts, I got the idea of communicating with them through touch. I wondered what would happen if I would compassionately touch a person where he felt the symptom in his body. Would that touch communicate with the part? Would the part become more resourceful? I decided to try it. The next time I was upset about something, I instructed a very compassionate friend in how to put her hand on my chest where I felt upset. The feeling went away. That single test didn't give me enough information to know for sure that a healing had taken place, but it encouraged me to investigate. And it let me know I could get a significant emotional shift with touch. I had formed the foundation for the development of Generative Touch.

Chapter Three

Touch

Generative Touch takes the pain out of painful memories, dissolves negative emotions to make room for positive ones, heals the emotional pain of physical abuse, replaces negative beliefs with positive ones, removes obstacles to success, and reduces physical pain.

How Touch Takes the Pain Out of Painful Memories

We store our memories in our brains and our bodies. Memories have emotions tied to them, and though the brain stores emotions in a special place reserved for that purpose, the body feels them, also. You can check this out in your own experience. When you're afraid, your heart may pound; when you're tense, your head may ache. So we know the brain communicates with the body.

Communication goes the other way, too—from the body to the brain. A gentle touch to the skin can create gentle feelings in the brain. A harsh touch can create fear or anger. I use this emotion-inducing effect of touch to change the feeling component of a memory. When I touch the person in a way that communicates a feeling of safety, that feeling is sent to his brain. If the brain feels safe while the person is thinking of the problem memory, it is free to tap into all of her resources and find a positive emotion to replace the negative one.

How Touch Dissolves Negative Emotions to Make Room for Positive Ones

We need the capacity to feel all of our emotions, including the unpleasant ones, because they can get us to act. What if there were something that should enrage you, but you weren't able to feel rage? You wouldn't know how to feel and you wouldn't take action. And that would be worse than rage. So in a way, unpleasant emotions are good. But you can have too much of a good thing. If rage lasts beyond its usefulness, it becomes a problem. It becomes a negative emotion in terms of how it affects our lives.

Negative emotions can be a signal to us that we need to change something about our lives. We may need to change our way of thinking or our way of living. Generative Touch gently changes the person's way of thinking, which spills over into his way of living.

Feelings of safety and fear can't exist in the same place at the same time, so when I touch my client with safety and acceptance on the area of the body that is connected to the part of the brain that is feeling fear, safety soon replaces fear. And when the brain feels safe, the part that felt fear can take the walls down and connect with resources that allow the negative emotion to be replaced with a positive one. The part soon realizes there is nothing to feel anxious, guilty, shameful, or afraid about and the person goes into a state of peace.

How Touch Heals the Emotional Pain of Physical Abuse

The body remembers where it has been hurt. That area of the body keeps sending painful reminders to the brain.

When I compassionately touch the area that was abused, my touch tells that part of the body it is safe, and it sends that message to the brain. When the brain feels safe, it lets go of the pain. The body relaxes and is able to feel again.

How Touch Changes Beliefs

Beliefs are made of words and feelings. Words tell us what the belief is; feelings make it stick—make it important—make it a belief. Without the feelings, it is just words. With the feelings, it is a belief.

Negative beliefs carry negative feelings. This type of touch sends a new, positive, feeling to the part of the brain that stores the belief. This changes the belief from a negative one to a positive one. When the feeling changes, the words change also, to match the feeling. Then you have a new belief.

How Touch Changes Attitudes

No one is born with a negative attitude. We learn them. We get them from painful experiences and we learn them from our elders. Negative attitudes are driven by negative beliefs and feelings. If I don't believe there is a problem with something or someone, and if I don't feel bad about it, I won't have a negative attitude. On the contrary, if I have positive beliefs and feelings, I'll have positive attitudes.

Negative attitudes can be driven by events in our past that we don't remember—we feel them but we don't remember them. This method of touch, since it starts with the feelings, doesn't require the client to remember the events. It goes right past the memory to the painful event and heals it, freeing the brain to adopt a new, more positive attitude and belief.

How Touch Removes Mental Obstacles to Success

Mental obstacles to success are often stored in the form of beliefs. When the beliefs are changed, the obstacles are removed. Thinking about what to do or what bad things might happen can create anxiety and fear. Touch resolves fears, fosters action, and allows success to flow easily and naturally.

How Touch Reduces Physical Pain

Pain is made of physical feelings and emotions. When I touch the person with compassion and acceptance, the body changes the emotion associated with the pain from negative to positive. Pain with a positive emotion is less intense than pain with a negative emotion.

Negative emotions can actually create pain by causing tension in the body. When I use touch to release the negative emotions, the emotionally induced tension is released and the pain is relieved.

Healing and Integrating with Parts

When we combine the idea of parts with the idea of replacing negative emotions with positive ones, we get the simple notion of helping parts feel good. When parts feel good, they take down the walls that have been separating them from our whole selves. With the walls down, they tap into all of our resources. And they re-unite with our whole selves.

As people continue to experience and practice this method of healing, they feel less scattered and confused. They feel more and more integrated—more and more whole.

Learning To Heal

In the next section you will read several demonstrations in which the principles in this chapter are used to heal real issues presented by seminar participants. The names have been changed and the transcripts were edited for clarity.

Watch the healing happen!

Chapter Four

I Want My Chocolate!

Heather Needs Her Sweets

We all enjoy eating, but sometimes it gets out of hand. And unlike smoking or drinking, we can't quit altogether. We have to continue to eat moderate amounts of nutritional food to stay alive and healthy. Sometimes compulsions arise, aimed at certain foods. When these compulsions are emotionally driven, we can treat them with touch. The compulsion may be driven by a long-forgotten memory. When we begin the healing, the memory may come to the surface. If you just keep your hand on your client, the memory will be healed and the compulsion will vanish.

Transcript

Heather: I really wish you would demonstrate what to do with a compulsion.

John: Okay. Who has one?

Heather: Me.

John: Come on up.

Heather: Is an addiction a compulsion?

John: We don't need to make that distinction to do this process.

Heather: It's an excessive sort of thing.

John: Excessive, obsessive, compulsive, compulsion—are you doing too much of something?

Heather: Yes. Eating.

John: Anything in particular?

Heather: It's about fat.

John: You mean you like to eat fat?

Heather: No I don't like to eat fat. The compulsion is about eating sweets. Okay… unlimited sweets.

John: And does it matter what sweet it is?

Heather: Yes.

John: You have certain sweets that are preferred?

Heather: Right.

John: Which ones do you prefer?

Heather: *(Lovingly.)* Chunky milk chocolate and hot fudge sundaes.

John: Good. I love to talk to people about food they love. *(Matches Heather's tone and tempo.)* Chunky milk chocolate and hot fudge sundaes. Anything else?

Heather: *(Warmly)* Frozen yogurt.

John: *(Continues in the same tone.)* Frozen yogurt. What flavor?

Heather: Chocolate.

John: *(To group.)* I have two purposes in asking her for these specifics. One is to get her into the experience. I want to get her in touch with the feeling of desire so that she will know where she feels it in her body. The other is to get information about how she looks, sounds, and acts while she still has the compulsion, so I can compare to what I see and hear after the healing to know if she has made a shift. When the compulsion is gone, she won't look, sound and act like she does now. *(To Heather, slowly and warmly.)* Chunky milk chocolate, hot fudge sundaes, frozen yogurt…

Heather: That covers it.

John: Let's start with the one that's most compulsive. If we do that, then the others will…

Heather: Right, because it's… *(Her voice becomes strained.)* I'm already anxious, thinking about it being taken away.

John: If it was taken away, you'd want to keep something?

Heather: Yes!

John: I'm guessing it would put you more at ease to know that if you still wanted to have it, you could. It's not going to be taken away, actually.

Heather: Just the compulsion will be taken away.

John: Right. When I dissolved my doughnut compulsion, nobody took doughnuts away from me. I'm just not compelled anymore. I can still have a doughnut. In fact I can still have the doughnut or not have the doughnut. I now have the choice. Plus I have the choice of eating one instead of four.

Heather: Right, okay, I got it. I don't want to have to eat two quarts of Dairy Queen ice cream and one of those big jars of Smuckers hot fudge that you heat in the microwave and pour over it.

John: *(Enticingly.)* No, but it sounds really good. I had the greatest hot fudge sundae the other day.

Heather: I'm salivating.

John: *(To group.)* We're continuing to notice how she acts and talks when she thinks of these special foods aren't we? Be sure to do that with your clients, so you can notice how they change

29

with the healing. Their physiological changes tell you as much about the effect of your treatment as their words.

Heather: As I think about those foods, I feel anxious.

John: Do you see any pictures in your mind?

Heather: Yes. Scarcity and 'not enough.'

John: Do you get any other pictures?

Heather: I have a picture of an empty cupboard. A picture of my mother.

John: How old are you in the picture?

Heather: Three.

John: Just you and your mother are there?

Heather: Yes.

John: And what's going on?

Heather: There's nothing in the cupboard. It's World War II.

John: And what are you feeling?

Heather: I'm feeling really frightened and anxious that there isn't anything in the cupboard to eat. There are no treats. Treats are the only way I know my mother loves me. That's the only way she shows love.

John: As you feel frightened and anxious, where do you feel them?

Heather: There, the same old place. Knots right there in my stomach.

John: May I put my hand there?

Heather: Sure.

John: Like this?

Heather: Yes.

John: I'll put one back here too *(on her back)* if that's okay. *(Two minutes pass, then John speaks slowly and soothingly.)* I want you to let that three-year-old part know that you are here for her... and I am, too... and that we'll be here as long as she needs us... and it's safe now... she's safe now... we're here to keep her safe... and we'll stay here... and we won't go away... I won't go away until she wants me to... and you'll always be here for her... Just let her know that she can always count on you to be here for her... and it's nice to know, isn't it?

Heather: Yes. *(Several minutes pass.)*

Heather: It feels good. Keep your hand there.

John: Okay. *(Three minutes pass.)*

Heather: *(Breathes deeply.)* It's complete now. *(John pauses to give her a few moments to come back to the present.)*

Heather: The voices were saying, "There's not going to be enough. You won't be able to make it," and as you put your hands—the one on my stomach and then the one on my back—the voices that were saying "It's not enough," were decreasing in volume and these other voices were intensifying and I was so caught up in that, that that's where I was. I was in there with that. You know it was like I was watching, too. It was...

John: You were watching... what?

Heather: I was watching the voices because I'm visual. And I was aware of this set of voices on the right diminishing in intensity and this set of voices on the left increasing in volume.

John: So, this set on the right was saying what? "There's not enough"?

Heather: "Never enough. You can't do it. It's the only way you're ever going to get love from your mother." The left side is saying, "You don't need it anyhow. You can take care of yourself. The universe will help you." It was gradually intensifying in volume while the right side was getting smaller, saying, "You can't handle your own loneliness by yourself. You aren't enough and the universe won't provide for you." It was an interesting transaction happening between the two sides.

31

New Feelings and New Beliefs

John: Now that the process has taken place, how is it for you?

Heather: I'm focused now. It's like it's right… here… *(Gestures in front of her.)* but in place of the hole, there's something warm… and I experience it as light.

John: Are there two voices now or one?

Heather: Just your basic, "It's all right. You can do it."

John: Now I want to know about the hot fudge sundae.

Heather: *(Unenthusiastically.)* It doesn't have the same zing.

John: *(Matching her tone.)* Doesn't have the same zing. What does it have instead?

Heather: It just doesn't excite me one way or the other. Like you were saying about the doughnuts. You can take them or leave them alone.

John: You could take it, you could go enjoy one, or you could pass it by?

Heather: Yes.

John: And how about the frozen yogurt?

Heather: *(Voice flat.)* No, it's all the same. I associate all those things the same way.

John: If you look into the future, I'm curious which way you look when you look into the future.

Heather: There. *(Looks to the right.)*

John: Just to cement this even more permanently, I want you to look into the future and see opportunities to have those food products. See the stores or see however you would represent them. And now I want you to see yourself, see a picture of you, walking or driving, moving forward into those situations…

Heather: I see myself walking by the door this way. It's like I'm walking right on by.

John: As you look at that picture of yourself in the future, is she saying anything to herself or is she...

Heather: No, most of the time she's not even thinking about it. She doesn't...it doesn't register.

John: Okay, good. And do you want that to go on for the rest of your life?

Heather: Yes.

John: Okay, see that going on for the rest of your life.

Heather: I'm going by it.

John: Okay.

Heather: I'm still walking.

John: We've created a movie of that aspect of the rest of your life. Now I want you to step into that movie, and instead of seeing yourself, you're in it, looking out of your own eyes. And just go through that same movie again, centered, taking care of yourself and letting those things go right on by for the rest of your life... *(She closes her eyes for a few moments.)* Okay, now come back to the present. Now, I want to know, is there anything, anything of that nature that could still hook you?

Heather: I don't think so. I'm real clear that when I want that, that's not what I really want. And when I wanted ice cream, that wasn't what I really wanted.

John: Yes, you wanted something else and now you have that.

Heather: *(Delighted.)* Right. That's amazing!

John: Let's do one other thing. Let's go back to age three with this new warm feeling. Can I put my hand back here a minute just to help you get the feeling? *(She nods and he places his hand on her back.)* Now at age three, look forward through time with this new warm feeling. See yourself going from age three up to the present with this feeling inside of you all the time. And notice how the meaning of life changes appropriately—that aspect of the meaning of life...*(John gives her time to enjoy the experience.)*

Okay, now go back to age three again. Step into it. And, instead of seeing yourself, you're in your body seeing out of your eyes...and go up through that time span again and really feel how it is, having this feeling with you all the time. And then you can—if you want to—let that process continue for a minute or two. *(Three minutes pass.)*

Heather: *(Opens her eyes, beaming.)* Thank you.

John: Thank you.

Do Changes Last?

Man: Does this need to be done periodically to reinforce it or does it seem to stay?

John: I can answer that with a story about my house. I used to live in a beautiful 2-story, 4-bedroom home with rough-sawn cedar siding, oriental rugs, and stone walks, sitting on a wooded lot. When I moved out of my house, I missed it and I felt bad when I thought about it. I saw in my mind the front of the house with the landscaping, the coach lights, the stone porch, and I felt sad. I used a mental process to change my feelings about that picture of the house. But two weeks later I found myself still feeling bad when I thought about the home I had left. How could that be? I came to realize that I was remembering the family room, the deck, the side porch, the bedroom, the powder room, the workshop, et cetera. So, although I had changed my feelings about the picture of the front of the house, seeing pictures of other parts of the house could still make me feel bad.

So I changed my response to several of those pictures and

after doing about ten of them, I could think about my house and feel okay. After living in that house for 10 years, there must have been millions of pictures of that house in my mind. I processed about ten of those pictures and the other hundred million took care of themselves. That's pretty efficient. We are complex and issues can come back, but it doesn't mean that the process didn't work. It just means something else needs to be done.

Man: It doesn't take away any of the power of the process or technique.

John: Right, so when you need more processing, find a person with a compassionate and gentle touch who will stay with you, who will leave her hand there as long as needed, patiently, and who will trust that you know what you need. In this training you have learned how to find the feeling. You know what quality of touch you need. You know if you're getting it or not, and you know when your processing is done. You can use all of that knowledge to get healings in the future.

How Words Speed Healing

Another Man: It doesn't seem to me that touch would make a significant difference unless you were using some type of auditory therapy at the same time. Coupled with touch, that would seem to be very, very powerful. But you would need that as a coupling factor to make it work.

John: Using words along with touch does make a difference. We ask questions of the client to find out what is the issue. We also talk to the part, letting it know it is safe and loved.

But it's also clear that the method will work without words. Sometimes the changes happen so fast that I don't get a chance to use words. Other times words are not appropriate or necessary. I typically do not use words when I'm changing beliefs because I want the person to come up with the new belief without my influence.

Genius is believing your idea may be as good as anyone else's. So, when you do this process, do what seems right for you. Believe that your idea may be good and do it. Find out. One test is worth a thousand expert opinions. So, test your ideas; find out what you get.

Let's talk about specific language. First, we thank the part and express appreciation. And we let the part know that you and I are there for it as long as it needs us and that you'll be there for it forever. That language can make the process go faster. If I'm working with a client and change is not happening, I say those words softly. Often it will cause a shift. The parts are often frightened and they need to know it's safe to come back. We stay with the part physically and let it know, by telling it, that "We're with you now and we will be with you all the way back through time to the original event and you will find out that you're safe there."

Chapter Five

Nagging!
Can It Be Stopped?

Why Is Sherry Bugging Her Kids?

Sherry is a mother in her fifties who wants to help her son
and daughter-in-law make wise spending decisions. But since the
young man and woman have ideas of their own, Sherry's suggestions often create tension in the family. Sherry would like to stop
controlling, but she doesn't know how. A force in her just seems
to "make her do it."

Desire To Control: A Feeling That Can Be Changed

It is natural for humans to want to control their environment. Unfortunately they often want to control other people,
too. Since people don't want to be controlled, conflict results.

The desire to control is a feeling. People frequently link emotions with bodily feelings, saying, "I want it so badly I can taste
it!" or "I can feel it in my bones!"

Feelings of desire dwell in the mind and in the body. You can
test this for yourself in your own body by doing a simple experiment. Think of something you really, really want. Then notice
the physical sensation you feel that lets you know you want this
thing. Just notice where in your body you have the feeling of

wanting. If what you want is good for you, it's best to keep this feeling of desire. If what you want is causing you trouble, it may benefit you to find a way to unshackle yourself from this feeling.

Transcript

John: Let's do another demonstration. We need a volunteer and we'll do one issue.

Sherry volunteers.

Sherry: Do I sit next to you?

John: Yes, I'll need you close to me because I'm going to touch you, if I have your permission.

Sherry: *(Sits.)* I've changed my issue from the one I put down on my list to the controlling one. I figure, "Go for it."

John: Okay, right now I want you to think of a specific situation where you got into that controlling behavior. Tell us a little bit about what was going on.

Sherry: Being a mother and mother-in-law and having more experience than my son and daughter-in-law, I make suggestions that I know are more practical than what they've come up with. Like where to buy plane tickets at a cheaper rate. Do I let them pay two or three hundred dollars more or do I make a suggestion to them?

John: As I see you describe this, it doesn't look to me like it's a problem for you.

Sherry: It is a problem. As the boys are growing up I make suggestions that they deliberately don't follow. I just keep nagging at them: "You know, you really should think that over." "That blue suit looks much nicer on you than the other one." "What do you mean, that's what the other people are wearing? Jean jackets for graduation?"

John: *(To the group.)* She looks pretty serious. This situation is not something that delights her.

John: *(To Sherry.)* Where do you feel this desire to control?

Sherry: I can feel it here, *(Gestures to her chest.)* and I know my hands are like this, *(Wrings her hands.)* thinking about it. I want them to buy the tickets that I picked out rather than the tickets that they had and that they want to get. Whenever anybody says to me, "Are you trying to control this situation?" I say, "No, I'm not. They can do anything they want." But, it's a struggle for me to keep my hands off and let them make their own mistakes and not make their decisions for them, even though they're not little children anymore.

Even if I talk softly and say, "Think it over, let me know," in my heart I'm thinking there is only one decision that should be made: my way, because it's much more logical and practical. And even as we speak, I can feel myself flushing down the back of my neck.

John: At this point you don't quite know what to do about it? You're not comfortable with either alternative?

Sherry: No, I don't want them working that hard for that much money to have it just blown away because they're not paying attention to the more practical way to do something.

John: Thank you for sharing that. *(To group.)* Now, as you look at her facial expression and her body movement, you can see that she's upset about this. She cares. So, before we use Generative Touch, let's think about what it would be like to use other means to solve this problem: we could discuss it, reason with her, use Neuro-Linguistic Programming or psychotherapy. To use any of those approaches, we would find out how she is thinking about it now, how she wants it to be, then develop an intervention. I'm not going to use any of those methods. Touch is easier than any of them because to resolve the issue with touch we need only know where the feeling presents itself in the body.

41

So let's do that and see what happens.

(To Sherry.) When you're in this feeling, being tugged both ways, where do you feel it? *(She points to several locations on her body.)* I'll need to know where to start since I can't touch all those areas at once. You probably have a sense of where the starting point would be. *(She points to two places on her chest.)* I can get behind you and touch both sides of your chest like this.

Sherry: Try one hand in front and one in back. Them we'll have it corralled.

John: *(Places one hand on her upper chest.)* Okay, now I want you to correct the position of my hand. Adjust my hand to let me know where it needs to be. It can go down, up, over, spread out. So I'll put it where it seems best to me and then you...

Sherry: That's good.

John: Okay, I'll do this too. *(John places his hand on her upper back. A long pause. Sherry's expression gradually changes.)*

Sherry: Can I volunteer something?

John: Sure.

Sherry: Okay, along with that issue, I thought of a similar issue that would be number two on my list. Somebody in my massage class said to me, "You're trying to control this ticket situation." I said, "No, I'm not. It's up to them." In spite of my denial she said, "Well, I have an affirmation you might want to try." And I thought, "I'm not going to use the affirmation because I'm not trying to control this situation," which was a controlling behavior right there. So the ticket problem doesn't mean much to me right now and I quickly slid this controlling issue right in next to it.

John: Those are probably two manifestations of the same issue. You can include as many as you want right now.

Sherry: As soon as you put your hands on me, the ticket issue really didn't matter that much anymore. I didn't want to waste any time on it so I slid the other one in.

Man: You certainly don't look sad anymore, that's for sure.

Sherry: *(To man.)* If he wants to do what he's doing, that's fine with me.

John: If you have more issues come up in the same place…

Sherry: Okay, I have one that I wouldn't have thought of; it's a controlling thing. Trying to get somebody to do something they don't want to do and I know it is for their own good. I want to know how to get rid of it. I mean not get rid of it, but an alternative. *(John keeps his hands on her chest and back for a few moments, saying nothing. Sherry's expression becomes more pleasant.)*

When I feel that need to give them advice on what they ought to be doing, I'll just send them the white light instead and let it go. That's action for me and they don't have to answer me back. *(John removes his hands.)*

Checking the Results

John: So, there was the ticket issue, then how about the other one—the one about controlling? What comes out on that one?

Sherry: I can't even remember it. I don't feel like it's a problem.

John: Will you stay up here for a minute for discussion?

Sherry: Yes.

John: *(To group.)* Okay. How long do you think it would have taken to solve that problem using some other form of therapy?

Man: About ten sessions.

John: *(To Sherry.)* What lets you know—I mean how are you

convinced—that it's going to be different?

Sherry: It just feels very light and airy here, *(Gestures to her chest.)* where it was previously very hot and heavy. It still feels light, you know.

John: How long have you had this issue before today?

Sherry: Well, I have to take off the first couple of years until I got to the terrible two's, right?

John: Ever since about two years old?

Sherry: I think it's not totally unique with me.

John: No, it isn't. You just happen to be the person who's up here for the demonstration. It's not unusual for us to resolve long-standing issues with this method.

Sherry: Yes, long-standing. I figure I was a pretty cheerful, friendly, one-year-old child, but once I got to be two I kind of wanted to do it my way, and that never changed. As I got older, I thought I was getting smarter and knew more than they did. I thought they would want to listen to me and do what I said. But now that doesn't seem to matter very much.

Follow-up Interview, Three Years Later

John: Do you remember the demonstration in the Generative Touch seminar?

Sherry: I remember where I was sitting, but I don't remember the main point.

John: It was about wanting to control people.

Sherry: I don't remember.

John: Airline tickets? Your son and daughter-in-law?

Sherry: Just vaguely there. The airline tickets would be the L.A. son and daughter-in-law.

John: It was about controlling. *(I read some of the transcript to her and she began to remember.)*

Sherry: It's familiar to me now.

John: How are you feeling about this now?

Sherry: That's why it was so hard for me to remember. Because I cannot remember being so controlling.

John: Oh, really?

Sherry: It's not an issue any more. I can stay out of it and realize everybody's in their own space and it's not my issue. Consequently, the end result is that they are looking to me to stop them from doing what they already know they shouldn't be doing, and it's like I don't care, so they can come up with probably the same decision all by themselves.

John: That's nice. How has that affected your relationship with them?

Sherry: Good to excellent. It wasn't that I had a bad relationship with them; it's just that that's where we locked horns.

John: So now that issue is gone?

Sherry: Yes. To the point that I could not remember. Then I knew when you said the airplane tickets. I remembered that I used to be upset if I could get the tickets for $250 and they were going to spend $600. I was upset that they didn't call and see if Mom had a solution for that. Then I would be upset that they hadn't called and checked it out because you know I can always figure out an easier way to get tickets or something. And now it's just...you remember when you used to carry your blanket around with you? Sure, I must have, but I don't do that anymore.

John: That's good to hear.

Sherry: Right. I'm sorry it took so long to elicit it.

John: Actually, that's good. It shows how thoroughly the issue was taken care of. Thank you.

Chapter Six

Bill's Aching Back

Can We Cure It?

I knew from working with the person who had knots in her back (See Chapter 1) that my touch could relieve pain. So, when I had a pain in my elbow, I decided to experiment with touch. My friend put her hands on my elbow, but the pain persisted. So she said, "I would like the part that's responsible for this pain to let me know where it is." The part responded by giving me a feeling in my upper arm. I told my friend where the feeling was, she put her hand there, and the elbow felt better in a few minutes. From that experience I learned that the location of the part can be different from the location of the pain.

What causes pain anyway? Why can't we work at the computer, do our gardening, and play tennis without having pain? Some pain is from trauma or poor posture, but other pain may come from repressed urges. Have you ever felt like you wanted do something, but you didn't do it? Perhaps you even tried to ignore the urge? It seems that our parts first speak to us with thoughts, ideas, or urges. And we have a choice of responding to these communications or ignoring them. Some of these urges are really important in our lives and if we ignore them long enough, the part then starts giving us physical symptoms—headache, backache, neck ache, sciatica—and if we ignore the symptoms long enough, sometimes the part takes another step and introduces a more serious illness like arthritis, cancer or multiple sclerosis. So it's better to respond quickly to the part's message.

But sometimes we don't want to respond. Sometimes we're annoyed at the part for causing us so much pain. Sometimes we forget that parts actually want to help us. So sometimes we do our best to ignore the parts and ignore the pain. A better route is to thank the part for what it wants for us and heal the part with touch. Then the part can stop causing pain. And as we let go of the pain, we often get new insights.

Transcript

John: Let's demonstrate the use of Generative Touch with physical symptoms. Does one of you have a physical symptom that you would like to heal?

Bill: I have a pain right here. *(He points to his upper back.)*

John: Okay. We can find out if the part is presenting itself at the same place as the pain or somewhere else. First of all I want you to thank the part because I know that all of your parts are wanting to do good things for you.

Bill: Wait a minute. I don't have a reason to thank that part because it's caused me pain for quite a while. So, I would have to be lying if I thanked it.

John: Perhaps a place to start would be to thank the part for getting your attention.

Bill: Okay.

John: And has this pain been going on for a while?

Bill: Yes, it has.

John: So, you could thank the part for being persistent.

Bill: *(Smiling.)* Yes. Okay.

John: Do you suppose that this part actually wants something positive for you?

Bill: I don't know.

John: I suppose the part knows.

Bill: Let me ask it.

John: Okay.

Bill: Yes. I got an answer. The part says, "Yes."

John: Do you want positive things for yourself?

Bill: Yes, I do.

John: Do you appreciate that this part wants something positive for you?

Bill: Yes, I do.

John: Are you ready to thank the part for that?

Bill: For wanting what it wants, yes. Yes, sure.

John: Is it okay with you if the part works toward what it wants for you?

Bill: Yes.

John: Is it okay if it gets your attention?

Bill: Well it's got my attention now. Sure.

John: Is this part feeling appreciated at all yet?

Bill: With the attention it has, yes.

John: Just let that part know that I appreciate it because I care about you and I like knowing that your parts want to do good things for you. And while we're talking to that part I wonder if it would tell us where it is?

Bill: The pain is back here *(Touches his back)* but the part says it's up here *(Touches back of his head)* and in my stomach.

John: Would that part like me to get in touch with it with my hand?

Bill: Yes.

John: Would it want me to start at the stomach or the head?

Bill: The head. *(John places his hand on Bill's head. Four minutes pass.)*

John: I'm just curious. Are you picking up anything? Do you have any idea what this is about?

Bill: No... well... wait. *(Surprised.)* This voice in my head just said it's about control. The words in my head are, "It's about control, not letting go." *(Two minutes pass.)* There's a part of me that's saying we're not in the right place.

John: This is not the right place?

Bill: I don't think so. The pain is right back in here. *(Points to his back.)*

John: May I touch you there?

Bill: Sure. That's where the pain is.

John: How about the part that's in your stomach? Do you want me to go there too?

Bill: Let's try it and see.

John: Okay. If it's the right place it should feel comforting to have my hand there. *(John shifts his hands. Four minutes pass.)*

Bill: Just hold on. Something is happening.

John: I just want you to let that part know that I'm here for it and I care about it and that it's safe.

Bill: The intensity is reduced considerably. Take your hands away. Let's see what... it's gone! *(Smiling, surprised.)*

John: Is it gone?

Bill: Yes!

John: Any other attendant changes?

Bill: I have feelings throughout my body. Typically I don't have many feelings in that area.

Discovering New Beliefs

John: Wonderful. Sometimes new beliefs are discovered when the pain goes away. Did your beliefs change at all?

Bill: Which beliefs?

John: I don't know. We didn't find out what they were before, so this is just a hunch. I'm just wondering.

Bill: Well, one belief I sensed was that I couldn't let go. Not that I was consciously holding on, but that's what my internal voice was saying—that it's about control, letting go. And I let go, so...

John: So, what's your belief now about letting go?

Bill: That I can let go.

John: Sometimes a new belief affects one's sense of self. Do you feel differently about who you are as a person?

Bill: Now I feel like I'm a person who can have fun.

John: Oh, really? I hear that's a good quality.

Bill: You know that's something that I've always admired about you.

John: I've heard that...

Bill: Yes, my partner, Connie. She's a fun person. *(Laughs.)*

John: Now you're a person who can have fun?

Bill: Yes.

John: What was the old belief?

Bill: That I couldn't have fun.

John: So, that belief changed just during this process?

Bill: During this process, yes.

John: *(To group.)* What we had was pain in the back or neck. When we solved it, a couple of beliefs changed also. From "I'm a person who can't have fun" to "I'm a person who can have fun."

What's the new belief about letting go? "It's okay to let go?"

Bill: Frankly I'm in a partial trance here. I'm in a fog. I'm not thinking.

John: That's okay. You don't need to. *(To group.)* We won't ask him any more questions. What would you like to move on to next?

Follow-up Interview, Two Years Later

John: We did a brief process two years ago in which you released some pain in your back and changed some beliefs about control and having fun. I wonder what was shifting during that process?

Bill: This was a number of years ago, but as I put myself back in that time and place, I remember I was resisting the Generative Touch process initially as I was up there. And I think at whatever point I let go and went with the flow is when the changes occurred. I had some internal dialogue saying, "This won't work." At some point I let go to the process. I probably said to myself, "Well, let's see. If it works, great. If it doesn't work, so what?"

John: So what do you think happened?

Bill: My guess is I let go; my body relaxed. And whether the energy flowed into the area or out of the area, I don't pretend to know, but the part was healed.

John: How about the belief about having to be in control?

Bill: It's something that operates out of my consciousness. I have a controller and protector part of me—a voice—that is the main part that governs me. I also have another part I call the pusher. I have another part I call the pleaser. Then I've got all my parents' parts—my critical mother and father parts. But the power self tends to be the controller/protector in my life.

Actually I'm working constantly to bring out the vulnerable parts of me, the parts that I disown, the opposites to the controller and protector. The person that can just let go and be present. But what certainly occurs is that when I walk into my company, my role is one of controller. And, you know, my controlling and bringing in technology has made my company successful. But the pusher part of me has suffered from the controller part and its need to control situations, to take over.

John: When you think back to the moment of healing, do you feel there was any shift in your ability to have fun?

Bill: I would guess that was related. If my belief is right, when I'm controlling, my body's going to tend to be rigid. When I'm doing a lot of head work, making a lot of decisions, that's when I think I have to be in control. When I come to the company and have to make a lot of decisions quickly, I tend to be in my head instead of my body and will have tightness in my upper shoulders and neck.

John: How about the part about having fun?

Bill: That was a part I had disowned. So that was a part I was trying to bring forward. I can't have fun while I'm trying to control. Having fun is being kid-like. The more the business is in order, the more fun I have because there's less I have to do. So my belief at this point is that if a healing presence were to touch me in that same area where I'm having pain, it will reduce. Then as long as I don't put myself back in a position that creates that, it's okay. But as soon as I go back to old behavior…

On the other hand, letting go, being present in the moment, being present to what's happening at the time relaxes my body and puts me in a softer state and opens the world to fun. I know enough about myself to know that I typically don't have fun when I'm trying to control things. The fun comes at times like walking on the beach at Myrtle Beach, just being there, hearing the waves, talking, giggling.

Control and fun have a direct relationship in my life as to how well we're doing business-wise. If we've got money in the bank, if we've got happy customers, and the bills are paid, I have fun. Or if I'm going to a place where I don't have to perform, then I can relax and be me.

John: Maybe it's trying to get control that's not fun. Once the system starts to do what you want it to do, you don't have to control it. You don't have to exert effort. And it's more fun.

Bill: Let it into the unconscious. Let it happen. This approach lets me do that.

Chapter Seven

Healing Horrible Memories

What Happened to Robin's Childhood?

Sometimes a person's emotion is not acceptable to her because it doesn't make sense. Or she believes it is somehow wrong to have that emotion. As a child, she may have been punished or laughed at for showing feelings. In adulthood, she may be afraid that others will shame her if she admits to having emotions. Yet the emotion is still there, making her life miserable. When a client comes to us bearing pain, we have a choice: We can simply heal the recent event or we can take the person back to the earlier event and heal the wounds that occurred then.

Certain signals tell me to take the person into the past. They are:

1) The problem as presented by the client sounds like a problem a child would have. For example, the client in this chapter says, "I never get to do what I want."

2) When she describes the problem, the client takes on the characteristics of a child. Her voice gets higher, for example, and her posture and movements match those of a child.

3) The client tells you this feeling was present in a past event.

4) Healing her in the present isn't getting results very fast. This cue is more difficult to sense because healings don't have standard lengths of time. After you have enough experience with the method, you will be able to sense when the healing isn't progressing. If you notice that healing is not progressing, you may want to take the client back in time to the original event.

Healing traumatic events from childhood does not cause us to lose those early memories; it just takes the pain out of them. A feeling that seems only annoying or inconvenient may, in fact, be tied to a hair-raising event from the past. Going back in time and healing the original wound can bring joy and meaning to life in the here and now.

Transcript

John: *(To group.)* Robin has a recurring feeling she would like to change. She has had this feeling as long as she can remember, so its origin was probably in early childhood. We're going to find the feeling now. *(To Robin.)* Here's what we're going to do, if you want to. First, I want you to think of a recent time when you've had this feeling. *(Robin quickly nods.)* You got it?

Robin: Yes. *(Robin gets teary-eyed and her face gets red.)*

Robin: *(Voice quavering.)* You can tell how I feel about it.

John: *(Soothingly.)* What is it about?

Robin: *(Upset.)* It's about doing things I have to do rather than what I want to do. It seems that I never get to do what I want. I'm always doing things I have to do. I don't like to admit this.

John: And with that feeling, we're going to go back to the first time you ever had that feeling. *(Speaking softly and slowly.)* Now I want you to let this feeling take you back... because this is not the first time you've had this feeling... so, just let that feeling take you back... and back... and back... way back... all the way back... very early... how old are you?

Robin: I'm just a baby.

John: Less than two? ... less than one?

Robin: Yes. Just a little after the newborn.

John: *(Very slowly and gently.)* And now at this age, I just want to know, where is that feeling? *(John pauses while she searches.)* Where is that feeling? *(John pauses again, giving Robin time to find the feeling. He gently repeats the question to keep her on task.)* Where is this feeling in your body?

Robin: It's on my, on this side of my head.

John: Okay. Is it okay if I put my hand there?

Robin: Yes.

John: Tension?

Robin: Yes. *(John holds his hand on her head for about 30 seconds. Then her posture shifts and relaxes, and her face brightens. John lifts his hand.)*

John: You can come back to the present. What happened?

Robin: It was like a...a lifting off of... or a taking away. A relaxation... a release. I don't now how else to describe it.

John: Okay. And with that "taking away," what does that change about your reality? How is the world different now?

Robin: It's brighter. I mean the picture I have is brighter.

John: How about beliefs? What do you believe now? *(Sometimes, when we heal emotional issues, our beliefs change also, including beliefs about who we are and what we can do, so John asks Robin if any beliefs changed for her. The questions help Robin put new feelings into words—words that state useful beliefs that will serve her later.)*

Robin: That I'm always working on the things that I want to do anyway.

John: Oh, really?! Okay, how about beliefs about yourself, about your identity?

Robin: That I have value and I have worth. I have a right to be.

John: How about beliefs about your capabilities?

Robin: Well, I can do it now. I will do it. Some of it's done.

John: And how about beliefs about the attitude of the universe toward you?

Robin: Acceptance.

John: Anything else?

Robin: Yes! *(She looks and sounds excited.)*

John: Something even better?

Robin: Yes.

John: Oh, goody!

Robin: Yes, that all my dreams are coming true.

John: How is that possible?

Robin: By uncovering the knowledge that was always there. Does that make any sense? It makes sense to me. I don't think it makes any sense to anybody else.

John: Yes, I think you're saying you have the knowledge inside.

Robin: Yes, yes! *(She is beaming.)*

John: Now let's find out. Look at item two on your list. *(John had previously asked the seminar participants to make a list of issues they wanted healed.)* Look at item three. What do you think about items two and three?

Robin: They all seem to have the same theme, obviously, since they're all under this one heading.

John: Are any of them still issues? *(She shakes her head no.)* Are you sure? You don't have to say no to please me or the group. If any of them are still issues, we can do them.

Robin: There's something here. *(She gestures toward her throat.)*

John: Do you want to handle it?

Robin: Yes. *(John places his hand on her throat.)*

John: Like that? *(She nods. A few seconds pass.)*

Robin: Yes. It's like it just opened up. *(Smiling.)*

John: Are you a happy camper now?

Robin: Yes, yes! *(She's really beaming now.)*

John: Do you have anything to say? Do you want to say anything?

Robin: No, other than it's… there's no words. I don't know how to put it into words.

John: Tell a story. It's like…

Robin: It's like when you were a little kid and you were hoping for some gift and what you got was incredibly beyond your expectations. That's what it's like.

John: That's nice.

Robin: That's what it's like. Oh, John! *(Glowing.)*

John: It's a great feeling.

Robin: Yes, it fits. Yes, that's what it's like.

John: Is it okay if the group asks you questions?

Robin: Yes.

Man: *(A seminar participant.)* Have you ever done this before? Healing with Generative Touch?

Robin: Not with Generative Touch. No.

Man: Do you believe there will be times when you're going

to have to do things you don't want to do? Times when you do want to do something else?

Robin: It's like this: Last Tuesday morning I went to work and looked at all the baloney on my desk and said, "Shit. I'd rather be someplace else doing something else." Now I know that the "something else" I can do is deal with the shit—which for me changes the whole frame and feeling about that issue and the rest of the issues on my list.

Woman: *(Another seminar participant.)* Are you aware of your face being soft and gentle?

Robin: I'm only aware that it just feels good.

Woman: That's how it looks to me.

John: How are you feeling?

Robin: I'm more energized. I have more resources. I have more energy. Even though I didn't get my seven hours of sleep and I was really tired when I came in this morning and I had that horrible headache. All of those things are gone.

John: *(To group.)* Any more questions for Robin?

Woman: I would like to ask how you know how old you were. You said it happened shortly after your birth.

Robin: I saw a picture of myself. Well, I was thinking, "You know, gee, I'd like to go back and see what a cute kid I was."

Woman: Can you just do it on command like that?

Robin: Oh, the work John and I did last night helped me go back. *(John had assisted Robin in resolving another issue the previous evening, using a method that did not involve touch.)* Last night I made a picture of the childhood situation over there *(Gestures to her right)*. So this time the easiest way to go back was to get that picture. It took a little bit longer last night to get the picture, but it was still there. In fact it was over there *(Gestures to her right.)* when we were talking about it today.

Man: *(A hypnotherapist.)* Okay. But that seems real quick to me. That's incredible how somebody goes back that far in time that fast. It takes me thirty minutes to get people back to that age.

Robin: It took something like two seconds.

John: You can take people back quickly when you use the language, tempo, and tonality you heard in this demonstration.

Comments

The issue we healed with Robin was intense and long-standing. When she was born, complications prevented her mother from going home from the hospital with her. Robin's father didn't want to care for a child, so he was not as kind to her as another father might have been. The issue we healed occurred one week after she was born. Forty years later, Robin was still carrying emotional wounds inflicted by her father. The wounded part presented feelings from those early wounds and allowed us to heal them, thus permitting Robin to access many wonderful new feelings and beliefs.

Follow-up Interview with Robin, Two Years Later

In this interview, Robin reveals her discovery that she was sexually abused as a child. She then explains how she used touch to heal these and other issues and how she has gone from numbness and lifelessness to new beginnings.

John: We did the healing without your telling us what the issue was. Do you remember what it was?

Robin: That young, I don't remember exactly what the event was, but I do remember there was something really big that I continued to hide from myself. The most important thing that happened during that session was taking away some of the layers so I could get to discovering and identifying the sexual abuse and incest that occurred when I was three years old. It was necessary to take the steps to work through eliminating some of the lesser issues so I could work through the bigger ones.

Using Generative Touch On Herself

Robin: I used touch to work through all of those things—the difficult birth, my mother's and father's attitudes about sex and children and more things that I'm discovering as I put some things together. I would naturally touch places where I hurt… and soon I felt better. When I have a headache or stomach ache or some pain I naturally touch it and it lessens and goes away.

So with all this crap about my employer and my job happening, I said, "You know, I really need to know what happened in my past so I can get that big part of it behind me so I can deal with the baloney that's going on now." In order to do that I put my hands on my lower abdomen, because I believe my body keeps my history and knows my history. As soon as I did that, I felt like I wanted to scream. I knew I couldn't scream because the windows were open and it was 4:30 in the morning and the neighbors would absolutely go berserk—you know, call the cops and who knows what else—so I kind of went inside myself and screamed and screamed and screamed and sobbed and sobbed and sobbed and sobbed.

I finally made it out of bed but I was hunched over and my arms were limp and I couldn't lift them. I couldn't move them. I just shuffled to the bathroom and shuffled downstairs and just sobbed and sobbed and sobbed and sobbed and then the thought crossed my mind as I was making the kitty's breakfast. I saw a knife on the counter. I looked at it and thought, "I could have killed that man if I'd had a knife."

At first it was shocking to me to have such a deep feeling of hatred. Then I got myself together and cried all the way to work. I was remembering the rape... My body was letting me remember, finally. Because of the rape, I had long ago stopped allowing myself to feel my feelings. And one of the reasons I had gone into therapy was because I kept describing my life as being lifeless. I was numb. I couldn't feel anything. For example, my nephew had run away and I didn't know where he was and I felt numb. I couldn't feel anything! Then the father of a woman here at work died and again I couldn't feel anything. That scared me.

So part of my understanding and my ability to recover my feelings came through healing with touch. I'm now allowing myself to feel the feelings I had when I was three years old. The Generative Touch experience accelerated my awareness and the healing process. And it's more than just making the hurt go away or feeling lighter or having a brighter picture. For me, the emotions are important because I have been so successful in numbing myself out, at least for the last 43 of my 46 years, and now I want to feel.

The processes opened a pathway, or an avenue. The way I described it is: I was really happy, although I was beginning to be suspicious when I started to realize that "I didn't know what I didn't know." Going through NLP and Generative Touch got me starting to know that I didn't know. And I've come to the point where I know—now—that I do know. And it has really made a significant change in my attitude toward life. For example, it has allowed me to openly accept and grasp the opportunity of losing my job and being paid to leave and not looking at it as if my life were over, but as if my life is just beginning!

* * *

Caution: Early childhood abuse can imprint emotions of unbelievable intensity and power. This method is a gentle approach to healing which does not require the person to relive the wounding experiences. If, however, you find your client overwhelmed by her past experiences, be prepared to maintain the touch for several minutes and sometimes several hours.

And remember, people are complex; although this method is very reliable, it does not work with some issues with some people. No method solves all problems with all people. So when any method you are using is not working in a particular circumstance, and you are concerned about the person's safety, please seek the help of an NLP Practitioner, a psychologist, a trained counselor, or a medical professional without delay.

Chapter Eight

I'm Not Good Enough

What's Jackie Ashamed Of?

Generative Touch can heal issues without the healer knowing what they are. The healer only needs to know where the client feels the issue in his body. To illustrate this point, I did this next demonstration without knowing anything about the issue other than the name of the feeling—and where she felt it. Only after the healing did I learn what the issue was.

John: Jackie would like to be the subject of the next demonstration. You can sit here and face the group. We can do this demonstration with or without knowing the issues. I suggest we do this one without much content so the group can focus on the physiological shifts and not be distracted by the content. Is that okay with you?

Jackie: Sure.

John: Okay. Just think of a specific time when you've had this feeling. Give us the name of the feeling. Just that much content.

Jackie: I call the feeling shame. It's sort of that never-enoughness or lack of protection or feeling of inadequacy. And it's a fear feeling.

John: Okay. You also know that to generalize the healing we

may need to heal the feeling in a number of different contexts to get the whole effect. Can you think of some other time when...

Jackie: Oh yes, I came up with ten troubling issues really fast.

John: Okay, now start to re-experience one of the times when you had that feeling. *(To group.)* I'm asking all of you to notice Jackie's breathing, posture, and facial expression as we did with Sherry. These are indicators of the emotional state she goes into when she re-experiences that event. Her mouth is kind of turned down. *(To Jackie.)* So, as you're in that experience, where do you feel that feeling?

Jackie: It's a knot right there. *(Gestures to her stomach.)* That's the fear in general. When I talk about this particular situation there's a knot in my stomach and a knot in my neck. Can it live in two places?

John: Yes, sometimes they are in two places. Sometimes touching either one will take care of it and sometimes it requires both. We just do what your body tells us. Which one would you like to start with?

Jackie: I'd like to start with the stomach. You think I'll be less fearful after you do this?

John: We'll see. May I put my hand there? *(She nods assent and he places his hand over her stomach.)* Do you want me to do it like you're doing it? With my fingers?

Jackie: No, I'd like the palm of your hand.

John: Okay. Would it be like this?

Jackie: That's good. It's interesting. This one *(stomach)* is decreasing and this one *(neck)* is intensifying.

John: Maybe it wants some attention up there. I can do this with my other hand, I think. I'm going to move closer. *(Places his hand on her neck.)* Just let your parts know they can change in ten seconds. Sherry's first one changed in one second. It changed quickly, so she brought up another one.

Sherry: It happened so fast I thought at first it didn't happen.

Jackie: There's a lot of heat. I can feel a lot of heat generating, just expanding. You can take your hand away from my stomach now. It's interesting because the heat was expanding in my neck. This one in my stomach is contracting, getting smaller and smaller but it's real tight.

John: Actually, I can do this. *(Places his other hand on her back.)* Is that better?

Jackie: Yes. It helps to have your other hand on my back. *(Ten seconds pass, then she says excitedly.)* It's gone. I feel clear.

John: It's gone already?

Jackie: *(More animated.)* Yes! It's funny how they were different. It's like they were going in different directions. I'll let you know Thursday night. That's when my group meets again. In one group I always walk out of there feeling inadequate as their leader, the group facilitator. So, if I don't carry that in my body when I go in, that might be interesting.

John: Let's gather some data right now. *(Speaking more and more slowly.)* Let's just imagine you're moving forward through time. Today's Saturday, *(John begins talking very slowly, allowing Jackie plenty of time to move mentally through time.)* and then there's Sunday... Monday... Tuesday... Wednesday... Thursday... and then it's Thursday evening. And just bring that group into that picture.

Jackie: Yes, I can see them.

John: And now turn that picture into a movie, and let the movie run as you go through the meeting. *(John pauses for several seconds, giving Jackie time to run the movie.)* What did you learn?

Jackie: I learned that for my part I have to be much more

71

concrete with this particular group and I have to go in there as if I know more than they do.

John: Connirae Andreas said, "I always assume somebody may know more about any part of the topic than I do. If they still want to hear me, I trust their judgment."

Jackie: I'll remember that.

John: Have your beliefs shifted?

Jackie: *(Firmly.)* Yes.

John: Before you go, may the group ask you a few questions?

Jackie: Yes.

Man: As you were running through next Thursday, did you have any feelings or sensations in the original areas or were they absent?

Jackie: Yes. They were like negatives of a photograph. I don't know how to explain it, but instead of the feeling, the sensation was like a shadow of it.

Man: More specifically, did you notice an absence of the feelings you would have felt in that situation?

Jackie: I noticed a brief presence of them, but it was as if that was enough. If you took a photograph of what we were working with, my experience of it when I made a movie of the upcoming meeting was as if that was the negative of the photograph. I don't know how else to explain it. I know that sounds unusual. I guess you could call it a shadow. It's like a shadow, but it didn't last. So, it was a blip and it was gone. My guess is that by Thursday, those feelings won't be there at all.

John: Your new way of being will help these changes last. You will have new experiences in the old situation. Then those new experiences will confirm the new way of living.

Jackie: *(Confidently.)* I believe that, absolutely. Thank you. *(Steps down.)*

John: There are many ways to get into the process I did with Jackie. The easiest way is to start with an emotion. Ask your client to recall the specific time and place when that emotion was present. It's not every time she goes to bridge club, it's a certain time she went to bridge club. We're not going after a general feeling; we're going after a specific incident. When we heal the emotion present in that specific incident, we heal that part of the person. That healing will affect all areas of the person's life in which that part is operating.

Jackie had been feeling shame, inadequacy, and "never-enoughness" when she led her Thursday-evening meetings, as well as in many other areas of her life. During the healing, she released the feelings of shame and inadequacy and replaced them with feelings of confidence and self-assurance. The shift was indicated not only by her words, but also by her facial expression, body posture and breathing. Her statement, "I feel clear," is typical of my clients after a healing.

Chapter Nine

Give Me A New Life!

What To Do If You're Dumb

Danielle: This is a story about a little girl. This little girl was about six years old and she believed she was dumb. Really dumb. And she had all kinds of confirmation of this because the people around her were really good at telling her she didn't do things right and she was slow to learn and she didn't listen well et cetera, et cetera, et cetera. In school, she used to sit on the thinking bench where she'd have to go when she was really bad, distracting other kids and things like that. She grew up strongly believing that she was very stupid and very slow and had to cover for it in lots of ways.

This little girl was me and when I was in my master's program at Case Western Reserve I realized that this belief wasn't going to work for me very well. I was struggling. I was struggling to read. Reading was hard and everything was hard, and at one point John and Tamara came to visit and I was beside myself with stress and concern about how I was going to get my papers done, and my thesis was due and all of this stuff. And the interesting sequence of events was that finally John and Tamara were very loving and very focused and said, "Would you like to do something that could help you with this?" I remember John saying, "It sounds like a belief to me!" and I said, "What do you mean?" and he said, "Well…" and as he asked his questions, I got clear that I had very strong beliefs that I was not smart, I was not capable, and I didn't have what it took to handle the load. A whole belief network had built up.

Woman: Where you chose to go to school, too, would reinforce that. That school is notorious for that. They tear you down almost intentionally.

Danielle: Right. It seems that way. Yes, it was a setup. I had always set myself up so that there was too much stress and too much incoming information for me. I had built up a belief network within myself that I couldn't read well and I couldn't assimilate information and that everything was too much for me. As John helped me change my beliefs, I learned that all I had to do was chunk things down and recognize that, "I can handle this." So, the belief went from, "I'm stupid and not enough," to "I have unique intelligence," and "I can handle this." What a major shift! It changed my feelings. My anxiety level went down and the way I approached problems and challenges changed. Just using the word challenge instead of problem was a sign of having changed the belief. So I've now completed the master's program and many other things in addition. I know Generative Touch works and I know that at the level of belief is where the most healing takes place. So, thanks for letting me tell my story.

John: Thank you. And I think I saw some nods of agreement while you were telling it.

Woman: Oh, a lot of people can relate to that, I'm sure, and it's something that I'm committed to changing for the kids I work with, if they're willing to work with me. I work with the school teachers at our hospital now and eventually I would like to be even more of an educator. Because it's really sad how much human life and potential we waste by installing this horrifying belief structure in kids. There's so much potential for change.

John: Thank you. We can often find beliefs in ourselves that have been stopping us: beliefs about our worth, our abilities, and possibilities we have. When we change our beliefs, our lives change also.

Examples Of Limiting Beliefs:

I can't.

I never could.

I won't be able to.

I can't change.

It's my destiny.

I'm helpless.

It's hopeless.

I'm worthless.

I'm not doing enough.

I'll fail.

I don't deserve...

I'll be rejected.

I'll be hurt.

My husband (or wife) never did love me.

I can't learn this.

I can't express myself.

The world is a dangerous place.

Everybody just tries to cheat me.

I'm bad.

I'm an alcoholic.

I'm too old.

I'm too young.

Nobody would help me.

That wouldn't work.

Even if I did it, it probably wouldn't pay off.

If I started it, I wouldn't finish it.

And even if I finished, someone else would take it away from me.

What I do is never good enough.

I'm not worthwhile because I'm not perfect.

I have to be perfect.

It's not okay for me to be successful.

Rich people are bad.

I can't do what I want in life.

Someone else could do it better.

Nobody wants to hear what I have to say.

No matter how hard I try I'll be second.

I'll never be first, I'll be second (or last).

I'm not good enough to be first.

It's not okay to be pretty.

It's not okay to have money.

It's not okay to be smarter than other people.

I'm weaker than other people.

It's easier for other people.

I can't be a good person and make money.

I'll never amount to anything.

I'm not going anywhere from here.

I've done it this way all this time, I can't change now.

And if I did change, it would probably mess up the rest of my life, and anyhow, it would probably ruin my marriage or something.

I'll never get over my loss.

I will hurt like this forever.

Everything is too hard.

It's not worth it.

People will laugh.

Do any of these statements sound familiar to you?

One way to uncover limiting beliefs is to ask yourself these questions:

1. Is there something important that I've always wanted to be, have, or do that I haven't been able to achieve?

2. Would I like to be doing more with my life?

The following transcript is rather long, but I have chosen to include all of it because it covers many useful skills in finding and changing beliefs.

Can Danielle Get Married?

John: Have you found an issue you'd like to work on?

Danielle: Well, I thought of one. It's about marriage: "Marriage is not congruent with freedom." Or "Marriage is binding... like... smothering." This is a belief that, as long as I have it, I won't get married. You know what I'm saying? So, I have a part that wants to be married and have a family and I have a stronger part that wants freedom, independence, growth and expansion.

John: So, the belief is, "Marriage is...", which implies marriage has to be...

Danielle: Confining.

John: *(To Danielle and group.)* Another thing about beliefs:

opposing beliefs can reside in the same person. So we can—at one point—think we're wonderful and then—at another point—think we're worthless, depending on what's going on around us *(and in us)*. When we release the "I'm worthless" belief, we become free to go into the "I'm wonderful" belief. The positive beliefs about ourselves are in us, but we also have negative ones we can slip into. For some of us, simply thinking about achievement or happiness may cause us to slip into a negative belief such as "I can't be happy." If we dissolve the negative belief, then we can soar into the positive one. We want to dissolve Danielle's negative belief.

(To Danielle.) So, "Marriage has to be confining." If you got married, what would happen? You'd probably marry somebody who would make you cook all the time and lock the doors so you couldn't go out.

Danielle: Well, no, but I'd probably marry somebody who would get upset when I would do workshops or somebody who would get upset when I was really committed to my career and my work. You know what I'm saying? So, the guilt trips, the expectation of what a "good wife" is and that kind of stuff feels confining. I was married and that was hard to deal with, and then when the relationship became abusive, that was a different story and it was not hard to leave. But yes, I created a very confining marriage. It perfectly proved that what I thought, what I believed, was true.

John: So, let me see if I can summarize this. The belief is something like, "I wouldn't be able to do seminars," or "I wouldn't be able to develop my career."

Danielle: Right… without feeling guilty. "It would be selfish of me to want to enhance myself or my career." This so clearly goes back to little kid stuff and family. It's amazing.

John: "I wouldn't be able to enhance my career without feeling guilty?" And another belief, "He would be upset if I..."

Danielle: ...gave attention to other things outside the house, outside the family, outside of him. I wouldn't feel free.

John: "I wouldn't feel free because..." he would be upset?

Danielle: Yes.

John: So, we'll put that one up here. *(John writes the beliefs on a flip chart.)* What else goes with that? So, therefore "I can't get married."

Danielle: That's right, "Therefore I can't get married."

John: Is that the bottom line?

Danielle: No, I don't think so. There's a whole lot in there. Do you want other beliefs that go with this issue?

John: Yes, I do.

Bill: *(Bill is the participant who healed his back and stomach in Chapter 6.)* You wouldn't have to be married to feel guilty about enhancing yourself. If you were in any relationship...

Woman: That's not necessarily true. Marriage is a whole different context.

Danielle: Right. It would be in a marriage situation.

John: It sounds like there's a belief something like, "I can be controlled."

Danielle: Oh, that's a good one. Something about control too.

John: "If I did get married I would let him control me," or something along that line.

Danielle: Right. "I would be second."

Woman: It means giving up your own wants.

Danielle: It means more sacrifice than...

Woman: "A good wife sacrifices for her husband."

Danielle: Oh, God! She's got the zingers today!

Bill: For me it fits, too, that "I would not be in control."

Danielle: Yes, I would say, "I would not have control." It's true. I would not lose all control because I would still have some; but I would lose a lot.

John: *(To group.)* I'm watching Danielle as you offer suggestions. If she nods congruently, then it may match her belief.

So, Danielle, what do these beliefs do to your life? If you were to keep these beliefs and not get married because of them, what would that mean about your life?

Danielle: I'd be selfish.

John: So, "If I don't get married, I'm selfish?"

Danielle: Yes.

John: Okay.

Danielle: And I'd be lonely.

John: Okay. Now I'm also wondering, suppose you keep these beliefs and you do get married?

Other Woman: *(To Danielle.)* You're miserable.

Danielle: Right.

Other Woman: It would be hard to be happy in a marriage with that set of beliefs.

Danielle: It sure would. If I do get married I'm scared… and struggling.

John: So, "If I get married I'll be scared and struggling."

Danielle: Yes. *(Sighs.)*

John: We're getting a good set of beliefs. I like to get a whole list of beliefs for a couple of reasons. First, we change a couple of beliefs and then we ask if the others have changed. And also, if we change a series of beliefs, she may change her entire world view on the topic. Before we start making changes, are there any more beliefs? *(Pauses.)*

Does this relate to issues other than marriage? Do you see other issues in life popping up along with these?

Danielle: Trust. Losing control is another piece of it that's not related to marriage. The dangerous parts.

John: Yes, that's the kind of similarity I'm looking for. "If I take this job, I'll be controlled." "If I quit my job, I'll ..."

Danielle: Yes, "It's dangerous." "I'll lose control." "If I really do what I want to do, I'll feel guilty."

John: Yes, "If I go into this partnership, I'll be in second place."

Danielle: Umm Hmm!

John: That one works for Danielle.

Danielle: That's a kicker!

Summary of Danielle's Negative Beliefs

Let's step out of the transcript for a moment to look at Danielle's awesome array of limiting beliefs about marriage.

"Marriage has to be confining"

"I'd probably marry somebody who would get upset when I would do workshops or somebody who would get upset when I was real committed to my career and my work."

"I wouldn't be able to do seminars."

"I wouldn't be able to develop my career without feeling guilty."

"I'd feel guilty about enhancing my career."

"It would be selfish of me to want to enhance myself or my career."

"He would be upset if I gave attention to other things outside the house, outside the family, outside of him. I wouldn't feel free."

"I wouldn't feel free because he would be upset."

"Therefore, I can't get married."

"If I did get married I would let him control me."

"I would be second."

"A good wife sacrifices for her husband."

"I would not have control."

"If I don't get married, I'm selfish."

"If I get married I'll be scared and struggling."

"It's dangerous."

"I'll lose control."

"If I really do what I want to do, I'll feel guilty."

"If I go into this partnership, I'll be in second place."

"I wouldn't be able to set boundaries and meet my own needs."

"Intimacy is dangerous."

Now, back to the transcript.

Choosing a Pivotal Belief and Healing It

John: Let's start making changes. Where do you want to start?

Danielle: How about "I would be second." The one about disappearing as a shadow or placing other people's needs above my own. It ties in to beliefs about freedom, control, and guilt.

John: Good. *(To group.)* What I'm getting from her seems to be the pivotal belief. She's saying, "If I change this one, it may change others." *(To Danielle.)* So, step into this: "If I got married, I would be second."

(Pauses to give Danielle time to access the belief.) Where do you feel it?

Danielle: Right here. *(Gestures to the front of her head.)*

84

John: Would you like to change it?

Danielle: Umhmm.

John: May I put my hand there? Like that? *(He places one hand on her head, and then after a few seconds, puts the other one on her upper back, as if to support her.)*

Danielle: Umhmm. *(30 seconds pass. She begins to smile, then chuckle and finally she laughs.)*

John: Does this mean we're done?

Danielle: Yes! *(Animated, excited.)* That was funny. It was very fast. That was a fast change, John! Do you want to ask me another question or do you want me to make a comment?

John: Please make a comment.

Danielle Describes Her Experience

Danielle: Okay. That felt like… when you put your hand on my head I kind of felt "cry," like tears. I felt like this little kid that has been left out. You know the little kid that always asks, "What about me, what about me?" It's a part of me that I've gotten real clear about. Then when you put your hand just kind of spontaneously, intuitively on my back, it was like, "And this is who you are. And you're whole. You're all here and you don't need to worry about disappearing or anyone else ripping you off from your power." I felt like all this was coming through me. And then I started to laugh because it was real. I know that. It was a stronger belief. And with that shift, it was all different.

Bill: Can I ask a question?

Danielle: Sure.

Bill: Do you now feel marriage is non-confining?

Danielle: *(Her expression changes, and she continues, suddenly somber.)* It has less strength. That statement is less powerful.

Since I've been sitting here, the intensity has diminished. I wouldn't say it's gone. It still has a little energy in it.

John: *(To group.)* As we look at her, we can see she was having fun, but when Bill asked her that question, she got serious again. So we're not done.

As you go through this process, check your progress. Ask the client if the old belief is still true and as she answers, look at her physiology. Believe her physiology before you believe her words. Her unconscious responses, as indicated by her facial expression, her posture, and her tone of voice are truer messages about her progress. She could say, "Oh yes, that's fine. Marriage... I'm not worried about it." *(John intentionally looks worried as he says this.)* And seeing the worried look while hearing the positive words, we would know we needed to change more beliefs.

Bill: *(To Danielle.)* How do you know it changed—I saw the dramatic change—and when John touched you on your forehead what was taking place inside you?

Danielle: I got in touch with the little girl.

Bill: How old were you at that point?

Danielle: Five.

Bill: Then I saw the dramatic shift, though, when he placed his hand on your back. Did you stay at five then?

Danielle: No, I grew up.

Bill: My question is, is this necessarily about the belief change or just that Danielle's got certain emotions stored in her body and you're touching those spots?

How Beliefs are Stored and Why We Change More than One

John: It's both. Each belief is stored in the mind and body as a combination of words, sounds, pictures, and emotions. With Generative Touch we allow the belief to change by healing the emotional content of the belief. As the emotion changes, the words, sounds and pictures change also. When I touched Danielle's forehead and back, her feelings and her beliefs changed.

Danielle: Yes.

Bill: The reason I ask is because of your question. When you asked Danielle, did she now believe that marriage is not confining, she couldn't make that full statement. But yet some change definitely had occurred in her.

Woman: But isn't that why you change more than one belief? Like five or six beliefs to generalize the change? *(To Danielle.)* Which of those sentences or phrases would bother you now? You know what I mean? The one lost its intensity, but as you say some of the others, they may still give you strong feelings.

Danielle: Right. So, the belief I thought was pivotal may not have really been so pivotal. It was just the one I felt like working with at that moment.

John: In my experience, changing one belief doesn't change ten. It usually requires changing three or four or five.

Woman: *(To John.)* I was just thinking that you're only part way through the process and that as she goes through more of the beliefs, when she is done, marriage will be okay.

John: That's probably right. We'll see what happens.

Woman: Okay, I'm understanding the process.

John: Yes, that's where we are in the process. We're taking lots of time to do it and I think that's useful.

Man: Can I ask one more question? *(To Danielle.)* What did you see while this was going on?

Danielle: While he was touching me?

Man: Before or when you were identifying where it was and what it felt like, what did you see?

Danielle: I think it was primarily feeling oriented...

Man: You didn't see a picture of a little girl or...

Danielle: No, I became her. I was completely associated into the little girl.

Man: Were you seeing anything? I know the feeling was there, but were you seeing anything, also?

Danielle: Not during the process. I was very much into my feelings.

Changing More of Danielle's Beliefs

John: Let's take another belief.

Danielle: Okay. Let's take the guilt one. *(Looks at the flip chart and reads a belief.)* "I wouldn't be able to enhance my career without feeling guilty."

John: Are those exactly your words?

Danielle: No.

John: What would be your exact words?

Danielle: I'd switch it around to, "I'd feel guilty about enhancing my career." I notice it doesn't have as much punch as it did before.

John: Because there's already some shift from changing the other belief.

Danielle: *(Nods.)* There's some shift.

John: So, with the shift what would be the right words?

Danielle: It's all different. I don't know.

John: "I'd feel sort of guilty?"

Danielle: Guilty isn't even the word now.

Woman: Limited? At times?

Danielle: *(Smiles.)* You guys are good.

Man: We need your words.

Danielle: I know, but limited is right. What just came up was, "I wouldn't..." this is all different now. *(More decisively.)* "I wouldn't be strong enough to set boundaries and meet my own needs."

John: *(To group.)* We're getting conviction now, aren't we?

Danielle: Yes. This is more like it. It's like being able to stand up and say, "I need to take care of myself and this is what I need to do for my work, or whatever." So, the belief I want to work on is, "I wouldn't be able to set boundaries and meet my own needs." This ties into marriage, of course. I'm getting better with problems at work. I'm practicing daily. But when intimacy is involved it seems different, much different. Saying, "This is what I need," is hard for me.

John: *(Restating the belief to make sure it's the one Danielle wants to change.)* "I wouldn't be able to set boundaries and meet my own needs."

Danielle: Right, that's it.

John: Okay. We got it. She means it.

Danielle: Yes.

Repeating the Old Belief while Changing It

John: *(To group.)* I'm going to ask her to say it again while you listen very carefully to her tonality and tempo and watch her non-verbal communication as she says it. So, make a movie in your mind of how she looks now—what you see and hear as she says this.

Danielle: I wouldn't be able to set boundaries and meet my own needs.

John: Okay, thank you.

Danielle: You're welcome.

John: Okay, where do you feel that belief?

Danielle: Here and here. *(Touches her shoulder and her abdomen.)*

John: And as I touch you there, I want you to be saying that belief to yourself and also I want you to say it out loud once in a while so we can hear how it's sounding to you.

Danielle: Okay.

John: So, here and here? *(Places his hands where she has indicated.)* Go ahead and say your belief.

Danielle: I wouldn't be able to set boundaries or meet my own needs.

John: *(After about 30 seconds.)* Okay, again.

Danielle: I wouldn't be able to set boundaries or meet my own needs. *(Her voice sounds tentative.)*

John: Really?

Danielle: It's tough.

John: *(After another 30 seconds.)* Say it again.

Danielle: I wouldn't be able to set boundaries *(Laughing.)* or meet my own needs. Do I have to say it again?

John: What happens if you try to say it again?

Danielle: Well, the last time I said it in my head it all scrambled up.

John: So, is it done?

Danielle: Done.

John: So, amazingly enough, you can have the person repeating the belief while you're holding the place where she feels that belief and it gets harder for her to repeat the belief.

Danielle: It did. It got very hard. The fourth time, I couldn't remember the sentence. I tried to visualize what was up there and then it scrambled. So, it got harder.

Woman: So is your belief now, "I can…?"

Danielle: "…set boundaries and take care of meeting my own needs."

John: Is that the new belief? "I can set…"

Danielle: *(Very firmly.)* Yes. "I can set boundaries and meet my own needs."

Man: Did you stay your present age? Did you do any age regression?

Danielle: Not on that one. I was my current age.

John: I'd like you to look at the list and see what's the next belief you want to change.

Danielle: "Intimacy is dangerous."

John: Okay. Step into that. *(Pauses to give her time to get access to the belief.)* Where do you feel it? You can breathe, too.

Danielle: I didn't know I wasn't breathing. Throat. Heart.

John: Do you want to do both or one?

Danielle: Both.

John: Okay. *(Places his hands on her throat and heart.)* Tell me to move my hands if you need to.

Danielle: This is good. *(A few seconds pass.)* Okay, move the one over my heart to the back. *(Four minutes pass, and during the four minutes she guides John to move his hands from time to time. Gradually her body relaxes and more color comes into her face.)*

Hmm! Wow! That was interesting because when you first had your hands on my throat and on my back it was reminding me of how I feel when I'm getting really into an intimate relationship and I feel like this. *(Gives a scrunching gesture.)* So, then when I had you move here in back of the heart it was a lighter, more supportive sense. Then it was like something cleared in my throat. A big block cleared. And then it was an equal support on the front and back of the heart chakra and then it became a free-flowing "Yes it's open. Yes I'm vulnerable, and it's okay," type of feeling. So, it switched from, "Intimacy is danger-ous," to "Intimacy is intense and that's where my growth is." So, the "dangerous" shifted to "intense and growthful."

John: Thank you. *(To group.)* Danielle's new beliefs are: "This is who I am. And I'm whole. I'm all here and I don't need to worry about disappearing or anyone else ripping me off from my power." "I can set boundaries and meet my own needs." "Intimacy is intense and that's where my growth is."

Danielle: Yes. Thank you.

Follow up Interview with Danielle, Two Years Later

John: I know you're in a relationship now. Did the belief changes you made in the seminar have anything to do with your ability to be in this relationship?

Danielle: Yes, and it goes beyond that. I do want to get mar-ried and have a family. And now I'm considering what qualities I want in a husband. My father was a very good provider, so I grew up financially secure. And the person I'm in the relation-ship with is not so good in this area. He has held many different jobs and doesn't keep any of them. So I have been supporting him off and on for three years. So now I know I need to find a man I can count on to take care of me so that I can take off work for several months after I have each child.

The Generative Touch experience helped me get clear about what was blocking me from marriage. And being in this present relationship lets me see some things I don't want in a marriage. That's good because now I'm truly thinking about marriage and what I do and don't want. Because now I know that I can have what I want.

Is Maria Still Making Excuses?

Maria is an accomplished educator who was not reaching her goals as quickly as she wanted. She believed she had control over her behavior, but she discovered that she also had a limiting belief that was causing her to let minor interruptions serve as excuses to avoid her work. We changed that belief with less than one minute of touch.

John: Does anyone else want to participate in a demonstration?

Maria: Yes. *(Comes up and sits down next to John.)*

John: Thank you. Would you like to change a limiting belief, an emotional issue, or something else?

Maria: What else can I do?

John: In addition to changing a belief or healing an emotional issue, you can choose to heal a childhood issue.

Maria: I would like to change a frustration with myself.

John: Please tell us about it.

Maria: I believe I have control over what I do. Although I know that, sometimes I'm not able to do things as quickly as I would like or to reach the outcome as quickly as I feel I would like to.

John: If I ask a person what's true, often there is a part of her that believes the opposite. If the belief were totally not an issue, it wouldn't occur to her to state it as a belief. So when you say, "I believe I have control over what I do," I'm thinking there may be a part of you that doesn't believe you have control. *(John knew to ask her about the opposing belief because he saw something in her body movements that didn't match what she was saying. Her words were saying she has control over what she does. Her body was saying something else.)*

Maria: *(Nods.)* You're right! A part of me believes that I don't have control.

John: And I wonder if that part of you wants to be healed.

Maria: It does.

John: Where is that part? Where does it present itself?

Maria: Here. *(She points to her upper chest just above her heart.)*

John: What does that part believe?

Maria: "I can do it, but I don't know how." *(This is the limiting belief.)*

John: I'll write that down so we'll know we have it. *(Writes on flip chart, then sits down next to Maria.)* May I put my hand there?

Maria: Yes.

John: *(John places his hand over her heart.)* You can help me adjust it to get it at just the right place. Right there?

Maria: Yes.

John: *(John presses slightly with his palm.)* Place the palm right in there? *(John's intuition led him to press a little harder with the palm of his hand. With experience, your intuition will give you similar signals.)*

Maria: Yes.

(Now there is silence for 40 seconds. Then she takes hold of John's hand and adjusts its location slightly.)

John: Like that?

Maria: Yes. *(Silence for 16 more seconds.)*

John: There. *(Speaking to the group.)* See this? *(John is point-ing to the corners of her mouth starting to curl up. Suddenly, Maria laughs.)*

Maria: "You've got it! We've got it!" *(She speaks very loudly, then laughs and laughs.)*

John: *(To group.)* There's a shift we can easily detect. *(The purpose of this comment is to get the group to notice her movements and expression—in addition to her words—as part of the message that she has made a change.)*

Maria: Thank you! Suddenly, it was there. I was there! We were there. It's magic. *(She laughs some more.)* I'm really hot. My ears are ringing also. Wow! *(She pauses for 10 seconds.)* I feel a lit-tle bit disoriented, getting ... Umm. *(She smiles softly.)*

John: *(Speaking slowly and in an even rhythm.)* The integra-tion and processing can continue as many hours or days as they need to. As they progress, you will regain your orientation. *(This is a suggestion to her unconscious mind that she can continue pro-cessing after the session.)*

Maria: I feel so wonderful!

John: Please share with us. What's new? Is there a new belief or new feeling? *(When a person puts the new belief into words, it settles it in and makes it more real for the person.)*

Maria: Yes! *(Laughs.)*

John: What do you believe now?

Maria: I can get there. *(She looks straight ahead.)*

John: Do you see where you're going now?

Maria: Yes.

John: I hear conviction in your voice.

Maria: Yes! My goal was farther away before and it wasn't in the center. Now it's there. *(She points front and center.)* I feel the connection between here and there. It's not separated as it was before. It's all one. There's a connection that makes it all one. So although I have to get there, "I'm there already." Because I'm connected. *(Laughs.)* Wow, that's great. Thank you, John.

John: You're welcome.

Maria: Hmm! *(Smiling softly.)*

Follow-up Interview with Maria Six Months Later

John: What happened after the session?

Maria: I sat by the pool for three hours, processing the changes.

John: How have the changes affected you?

Maria: My perspective changed; my outlook changed. My vision became closer, centered, right in front of me *(gesturing.)* That changed my behavior. *(Speaking warmly.)* Since the vision is closer and clearer and centered, I am living from my heart.

Instead of being confined by delusions of my own creation, I am not captive anymore. I became more detached from things that were not in my best interest. I stopped sabotaging myself. I stopped reacting to obstacles that I was imagining. I've been able to do things in a more engaged and connected way, without the perceived difficulties that I had created before.

John: There were imaginary difficulties?

Maria: I thought they were real, but after I had the shift, I realized they were imaginary. For example, if I had to get a certain piece of writing done and the phone rang, I wouldn't do the writing. Then I would say, "The phone rang, this happened, and that happened, so I didn't get it done." Now I just stay with it until it's done. Before, I was making excuses about why it didn't happen.

John: And now?

Maria: *(Sounding matter-of-fact.)* I just do it. In essence, I moved from doing victim things to willing power over my own life…willing my own behavior… approaching the day in a more conscious way. I'm conscious of what is happening, what I'm doing, what my goals are, and how I'll approach them today. I was using too long a time frame before. Now it's, "This is for today. Tomorrow may be different. Today this is what I'm going to do… about x, y, or z." It's more directed and it's more flexible.

John: I like it. What has this new behavior added up to? Do you notice that the quality of your life has changed in some way?

Maria: Of course! I'm in control of it. I'm one with it. I'm not fighting it. *(Laughs.)* Those are the words I was looking for. I'm more in tune with myself. I was judging myself in a critical way that was sabotaging me. And I wasn't aware of it. That kept me away from being connected with my vision and living from my heart. Now I see the light.

John: Is it just a light or is something in the light?

Maria: *(Confidently.)* I see a white light and I know what's in there. My mission and purpose are in there. I am more connected with my mission and purpose and at one with them and with myself. I'm focused on my mission and purpose and I'm coming from my heart.

John: It sounds like it's all coming together now.

Maria: I wrote some short stories when I came back from the seminar, about things that just came up. The change may have stimulated them since there were three in a row. They are metaphors about my changes.

John: I would like to see them. Now that you're more connected with your mission and purpose, are you moving toward it more directly?

Maria: Oh, yes! I spend time getting in touch with my vision and purpose every day. I'm getting more work done.

John: What work?

Maria: All of it. All types. All that I do.

John: You're sounding very focused now.

Maria: That was very magical, I loved it very much. *(Laughs.)* That's just what I needed.

John: The whole touching process took less than a minute.

Maria: I can remember the whole thing. It seemed like nothing was happening and then I knew something was happening, but I didn't know how I was getting that signal and then suddenly, ZAP! *(Laughs)* That was great.

Now I take time for myself every morning and every evening. I bring flowers in, burn a candle, meditate and concentrate on my vision and my mission.

John: Is that something new for you?

Maria: Yes. It is new. It's nice to have the light and the aliveness of the flowers. They are special to me.

SECTION THREE

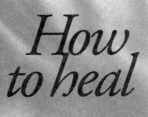

*How
to heal*

Chapter Ten

The Heart

When working with clients, friends, and relatives, it is necessary to go at their pace and gently encourage their hidden parts to emerge. As I prepare to heal with touch, I cultivate feelings of care and compassion for the part, thinking of it as a small innocent spirit. This state of mind leads me to always ask permission and to approach the person slowly, watching for his responses as I move my hand near the location he wants me to touch. When my hand gently alights on his body, my attitude is total and unconditional acceptance. My goal is to have the part feel safe and loved so it can let go of years of fear and pain.

Some parts have carried their pain for decades, perhaps since before the client learned to talk. Fortunately, you can use Generative Touch with pre-verbal issues. You can go back in time and resolve issues that impacted a person at the pre-verbal stage—things that happened before the child had the language skills to talk about them. As one client said, "If you want to change something that happened to a person before she was a year old or when she was in the womb, language doesn't make much sense to her. Touch does." When touching, your intention is to create safety for this pre-verbal child.

To communicate the feeling of love and safety, you'll want to touch the young parts like you would touch a young child. My friend Leslie, taught music to young children for many years. She knows how touch can facilitate communication with children: "With some kids you need to touch them to get their attention. When I touch them, I know that the quality of my touch affects the way they feel. They can feel my warmth and friendliness and also my authority. When you're working with kids, touch often communicates what you want to say more effectively than words alone. The younger the child, the more true this is. They may not get the message as strongly without you touching them. I have found the same to be true in my counseling and healing work with young parts and inner children of adults."

Touching with an attitude of compassion may even be therapeutic for people with mental disease. Have you seen the movie *Awakenings?* The film is based on the work of Oliver Sacks, noted psychiatrist, researcher and writer. Do you remember the scene near the end of the film when Leonard is in the cafeteria of the hospital and he is not able to hold his head still? He's with the lovely young woman whose father was a patient there. Leonard is acting strange; his whole body is shaking and he finds it impossible to form words. Then an astonishing thing happens. We see the young woman gently and lovingly take his hand in hers and put her arm around his waist. As she holds him, his shaking begins to subside. She helps him to stand and she starts dancing with him—and he stabilizes. Sacks showed us how compassionate touch can benefit even a deeply disturbed individual.

Healing with touch does not require intense mental concentration; softly I focus my attention on the person I am healing. My intention to heal is essential; it lets the part feel safe so it can let go of the hurt and pain. My attitude of gentleness and caring are felt by the part. As I keep my hand on my client, a part which begins with distrust and reluctance soon feels safe and is able to relax and heal.

Presuppositions that Give You Power

When I work with an individual or facilitate a group, my attitude is influenced by the presuppositions of neuro-linguistic programming. I assume that:

1) Behind every behavior, thought and feeling is a positive intention.

2) People can benefit from having more choices.

3) People work perfectly. No one is broken.

4) People have inside them the resources they need.

5) When I communicate with a person, his response lets me know what my message means to him.

6) Mind and body are elements of a single system.

7) Behavioral flexibility increases my probability of success.

8) We each make our own map of the world and operate as if it were accurate.

9) People make the best choices available to them at the time, given their mental state and their physical environment.

10) Communication takes place through sight, sound, taste, smell, and touch. All are operating all the time, even when some are out of awareness.

11) If one person can learn to do something, others can.

12) Anything can be accomplished if we break it down into small enough pieces.

These assumptions keep me in a state of positive expectation that supports my success with clients. Adopting them will enhance your success, too.

It is important to have rapport with your client when you're healing. Then, rather than only her being healed, you both are. That's one really nice aspect of doing this work. At the end of a Generative Touch session, both people feel refreshed and both receive healing.

Chapter Eleven

The Key

Breathing

One way to establish good rapport with your client is to match the pace of her breathing. You can follow a person's breathing by watching her shoulders or chest go up and down. Or you can watch the folds in her blouse expand and contract as she inhales and exhales. Then you can begin to breathe with her. I remember when I first breathed with a person, I felt like I was out of breath. I thought I couldn't get enough air. If you feel out of breath, just breathe more deeply. Then inhale and exhale at the same time as the other person. As you breathe together, you may feel a change in the ambiance of the room. You'll probably find yourself feeling more comfortable.

Breathing is a way to get rapport when just talking doesn't do it. Once I was having trouble getting rapport with an engineer who worked for me. I had talked with him about everything under the sun and our rapport only lasted as long as we talked about topics he was highly interested in. One day I decided to breathe with him. I sat to his left, about ten feet away. I held a notebook open as if I were reading, and I breathed with him. In five minutes he said, "Do you want to go to lunch?" I continued to breathe with him at lunch and after that we always got along well.

Breathing is a good way to get rapport with almost anyone. And it only takes a couple of minutes. If you stop and give a person your attention long enough to match her breathing, you're setting the stage for effective communication.

When I heal with touch and match breathing, I imagine what it would be like to receive the touch I am giving. That slows me down to a more effective pace. Slowing down helps me stay on an area until I have a sense of completion. I ask the client if that area is done. Only then do I move to the next area.

As you get more practice, you will gradually notice more of the needs, feelings, and wishes of your clients because you will be more in tune with them.

Caution: If the person has a breathing disorder such as asthma, don't breathe with him. Just breathe steadily.

Dealing With Anxiety

When I first healed with touch, I had lots of anxiety about whether it would work. Some of my students do too. A woman at one of my seminars said, "When I was working with my client, I recognized my biggest block. I had this continual performance expectation. Like, 'I need to do this really well. Is this what he wants? Maybe this isn't the way he wants it.' The internal chatter was just obnoxious. So I just said to myself, 'Let go; trust the process. I know intuitively what to do.' Then I became more effective. Then that chatter stuff would come back again—this, 'Am I doing okay?' type of feeling. I could recognize it because the frustration is there when the chattering is present."

Being in a state of anxiety doesn't promote rapport or healing, so if you have anxiety (and haven't already dissolved the feeling with touch) replace the chatter by giving attention to the feelings you're getting from your client. Give 90 percent of your attention to what's coming back to you from that person. That's the information that will let you know how you're doing. That's where the answer is. You can trust that the information you're getting is the information you need to know. You see what you see, you hear what you hear, you feel what you feel, and you trust that it's real. And ask questions of your client when you need to. You don't have to read her mind. Remember, it's a partnership. If you want to know what's going on with her, just ask. The information you get will help you gain deeper rapport.

You can also remember that you don't have to heal this person. It's okay if you don't. I know you want to, but you don't have to.

Several conditions could prevent healing.

1. The client may not be ready to be healed at this time.

2. The issue you are treating may take more time to heal than you have available.

3. You may not be in a state of mind to do healing right now.

4. You may not yet have the confidence or experience to take on the issue that's being presented to you at this time. When I was first doing this work, I put my hand on a woman's stomach for 20 minutes and the issue seemed to be getting worse instead of better. I abandoned Generative Touch and treated her with another method. I didn't yet have the confidence to stay with an issue that long. And I didn't know that issues sometimes seem to be getting worse before they get better. Now I know to stay with an issue until it is resolved.

5. The issue may be one that will not respond to this type of treatment. The client could have severe:

a) Neurological damage,

b) Mental illness

c) Physical degeneration (of the spine, for example.)

6. Your goal may be too high. Perhaps you can only reduce a person's pain, not eliminate it.

Your job is only to do the best you know how to do at the time.

Chapter Twelve

The Link

Parts create feelings in the body. To heal a part with touch, you must find the feeling and connect with it. You can practice this skill by yourself right now. Here's how to do it. Take a minute and think of a time when you were in a mildly unpleasant situation. Feel the feeling you were having at that time and notice where it presents itself in your body. If you feel it all over your body, just notice where it would focus if it were to center in one place. Then put your hand there.

Finding the Exact Location of the Feeling

Adjust the location of your hand to place it at the exact location of the feeling. Now take your hand away and let go of the feeling. We'll come back to it later. I want to ask you this: Did you have your hand exactly on the right place the first time? Or were you able to position it more precisely by moving it?

Now you know that you're good at finding the exact location of a feeling. Notice how precise it is. Your body puts the feeling in one exact place. You will discover such precise feelings in your clients and they will want you to place your hand in precisely the location of the feeling. Remember that you don't have to find the exact location alone. Your client will gladly help and direct you.

When you touch in this way, you have connected your unconscious mind with your client's through touch.

You may have cases where the emotion presents itself in more than one spot. Maybe you can reach them both at the same time. If not, just ask your client, "Which one would you like to do first?" Then touch that one.

Following the Feeling

Sometimes you'll touch one spot for a while and then another spot, previously unidentified, will come up. If it does, simply touch it the same way you did the first one. Sometimes the feeling will move in a line up or down the client's body. Other times, it will seem to move at random. As the client reports the feeling's movement to you, just follow it with your hand. This is a partnership. You're working together. If you are the client and the practitioner heals one spot and then you feel another one, ask the practitioner to put her hand there.

Before I developed this method, I was doing talk therapy with a client who had many issues that were linked together. We would begin with a single issue, but that issue would lead us to another and then another. It was a tremendous exercise in patience and perseverance to keep track of the issues. We weren't able to resolve any of them completely because related issues would arise and interfere with the process. The lack of success frustrated both of us. In contrast, when I used Generative Touch with her, keeping track of the issues was much simpler. I'd touch her in one place and as that issue resolved, another issue would pop up in another part of her body. With touch, I could follow her feelings—and issues—easily. We did more work and did it faster, and each issue was resolved in minutes. In a few hours we resolved a complex web of emotional issues that had been blocking her progress for years.

Intuition

From the beginning I often knew without asking where to touch a person and I knew intuitively when the healing was done. I wondered if I could teach people to heal with touch if they were not equally intuitive. By experimenting, I found that almost anyone can heal with touch, whether or not they know intuitively where to touch. You simply ask the person where she feels the emotion. You can use your intuition if you want to, and I'm sure you will as you gain experience, but it's not required.

Although your intuition may let you know when the healing is completed, there are also physiological signals such as breathing changes and muscle relaxation that indicate change has occurred.

With experience you will learn to notice the signals. And, of course, you can always ask your client.

Chapter Thirteen

The Healing

My relationships with the client and her parts are essential to healing. Whenever I speak to the client, I assume I am also speaking to her parts.

To build a relationship of safety and trust, I always give the part plenty of information about what I'm going to do before I do it. This starts when the client first comes into my office. I greet the client, ask if she wants a drink of water or anything, show her where to sit, and show her where I'll be sitting. I ask her what she wants out of the session and I find out what emotions or beliefs are stopping her from getting what she wants. Then I am ready to begin the healing.

I ask her if she would prefer to lie on the healing table or sit in a chair. When she is on the table or seated in the chair, I ask if she is comfortable, does she need a pillow or a cover. I look at her, listen to her voice, and check my own feelings to know if she is comfortable. Then I ask where she feels the emotion or belief in her body. I look at the place where she says she has the feeling, and ask her permission to touch her there. Then I put my hand over it and say, "Right here? How do you want my hand? I can put it like this, or this, or this," giving her several options. So I'm giving the part lots of choices before I touch it. This lets the part know it's in charge of the process; this helps it feel safe.

All of my words and movements consider the part's need to feel safe and be in control. I ask permission before I touch the client. I speak in a medium tempo and give the client choices every step of the way. I move at the same tempo at which I speak. The rule is to respond to the client, both verbally and non-verbally.

The quality of touch is critical to the healing. If you were in the seminar, you could see how I do it, but since you're not, I'll do the best I can to express my technique in words.

When I put my hand on the person, I do not move it at all. You cannot imagine how important that is. If the part feels my hand move, it has to interpret the meaning of that movement; it has to decide if it is a safe or a dangerous movement. It has to determine whether it needs to respond in any way to the movement. In contrast, if I am not moving at all, the part is relieved from those decisions and can fully relax into the healing.

When the client has indicated exactly how she wants my hand to be placed, I place it there and ask if I'm using the right amount of pressure. Sometimes when my hand is on a person, it feels as if her body is pulling my hand into it an eighth to a quarter of an inch. It's as if the part is saying "Hold on to me." I keep my hand there as long as I feel the body asking for it. As the healing progresses I can feel the client's body releasing my hand, allowing my hand to rise to the surface. When I feel that we're done I ask the client, "Are we done?"

I don't remove my hand without the client's agreement, even if it's just to stretch. Then I say, "I need to let go for a minute. I need to stretch and I'll be right back." When I have the client's assent, I gently and slowly remove my hand. After stretching, I say, "Is it okay to put it back?" With permission I again place my hand on her body.

When the client and I agree the healing is done, I remove my hand as slowly and as gently as I placed it there. I almost roll my hand off her body from the heel of my hand to the middle to the fingers. I lift it just an inch at first and watch her face to be sure she is comfortable without my hand. If her face shows any sense of loss or distress, I say, "It looks like we're not finished. Shall we continue?" and with her assent, I put my hand on her again.

During the entire process, I feel compassion for the part. I have an attitude of total and unconditional acceptance. It is innocent and defenseless. There is nothing to do but love this part. The part is more like a young spirit than like a young whole person. It's that pure. It's like an innocent little child that needs to be loved and cared for.

Although healing with touch is easy to do, I need to be rested and alert when I do it. So I don't start the process too late at night or too early in the morning. Some healings take only a minute. Others take an hour. When I have had my hands on a person for a half hour or so, I usually take a three-minute break after asking permission from the client.

Sometimes the healing process can be enhanced by talking to the part while I am touching the client. First, I thank the part and ask the client to express thanks for the part's positive intention. If the client doesn't want to do that at first, I mediate to help him appreciate the part. I let the part know that we are here for it as long as it needs us and that he (the client) will be here for it forever. Those words, spoken slowly and gently, sometimes make the process go faster. If I'm working with a client and change is not happening, I say those words. Often that will facilitate a shift. The part may be frightened; it needs to know if it is safe. I stay with the part physically through my touch and let it know, by saying so, that "we're with you now and we will be with you as long as you need us."

Here's an example of what I would say to a person with a three-year-old part to let it know it is safe and loved: "I want you to let this part know that you are here for her... and I am, too... and that we'll be here as long as she needs us... and it's safe now... she's safe now... we're here to keep her safe... and we'll stay here... and we won't go away... I won't go away until she wants me to... and you'll always be here for her... Let her know you're big now... a full-sized adult... and you have lots more power now... and you can take care of her and keep her safe... and let her know... she can always count on you... to be here for her... and it's nice to know... isn't it?"

Getting physically comfortable can enhance your work, too. It is often easiest to heal with touch with the person lying down. This physical arrangement is easier for you and it lets the client relax and release emotions and limiting beliefs from her muscles. When I first healed with touch, I would have the person lying crossways in front of me and I would sit cross-legged beside her. Now that I use a table, I just stand by the table. You can have the person lie on a couch, a bed, a massage table, or on the floor.

Have the client lie on her back or front, depending on where the issue presents itself. Most issues present themselves on the front of the person's body, so I like to begin with the person lying on his back. I take plenty of time to get myself situated so I can stay in one position as long as I need to. I make myself fully comfortable so that I will not need to wiggle around or shift my weight during the healing. If I move any part of my body during the healing, that movement travels through my body to my hand and the movement in my hand can disturb the part. Wounded, fearful parts need absolute steadiness to feel safe and heal.

Generative Touch works well without touching the skin directly. If the area of feeling is clothed, you can get completely satisfactory results by placing your hand on the person's clothing.

Be sure to stay on one area until it is healed. Did you ever have a massage and you wished the massage therapist would stay on an area for a while, but she moved on to other areas? The part connected with that area wasn't finished processing. It wanted more touch. The part was communicating with you, saying, "More! More!" When doing Generative Touch, we stay with the part until it's healed.

The quality of touch is important, too. The hummingbird flies lightly about and alights gently on the petal of a flower. Your hands can alight as gently on your client.

You are working with your client as a team. When you are ready to remove your hand, let your client know your intention, wait for her approval, and then remove your hand. When you remove your hand, do it as slowly and gently as you placed it there. Watch her face for any signs that the part wants your hand to stay there. It is important that the part be comfortable as it releases contact with your hand.

In section IV, you will write down lots of information about negative emotions and when you have them. The processes below can be used to heal them.

SPECIFIC INSTRUCTIONS FOR HEALING WITH GENERATIVE TOUCH

In the following sections, you will receive step-by-step instructions for resolving several types of issues. These instructions are written on the assumption that you have already read the rest of the book. If you haven't read the book, these instructions may not make sense to you and the process may not work.

If you attempt to follow the instructions and you don't get results, read the book again. Also, training seminars and audio tapes are available to help you refine your technique.

The first step in any of the processes is to get rapport with the client and get into a comfortable position. If your client is on a healing table, stand in a balanced, comfortable position or sit in a chair with both feet flat on the floor. If your client is sitting in a chair, you can stand, sit, or kneel next to her. If your client is lying on a couch or on the floor, sit on the floor or kneel by the couch. Or you can sit on the floor with your client lying in front of you.

At the end of each process, you will see a step called, "Release the bond between yourself and your client." This step is here because touch can create a bond that is closer than you want to maintain over time. To release this bond, look at your client and name (silently, to yourself) five things that make you different from your client, such as your age, sex, hair color, shoe size, etc. You may also wish to take on a different posture or to move differently from the way she does.

If you have taken on any of the client's negative energy, allow it to flow out through your feet into the earth to be recycled.

RESOLVING AN UNPLEASANT EMOTION

INSTRUCTIONS FOR THE PRACTITIONER

Refer to Chapter 8 for a demonstration of this process.

1. Get comfortable and match the person's breathing.

2. Elicit from your client the emotion she wants to resolve. Ask her to think of a specific situation in which she had that emotion.

3. Ask, "Where do you feel it in your body?"

4. Ask, "May I put my hand there?"

5. With permission, place your hand there.

6. Keep your hand there until you feel a shift that lets you believe the process is complete. You may see tension in her face

or body release as the emotion dissolves.

7. Ask, "Are we done?" If the answer is "Yes," remove your hand.

8. Be silent while she readjusts to the here and now.

9. Ask her to describe the results.

10. Release the bond between yourself and your client.

HEALING A PAINFUL MEMORY

INSTRUCTIONS FOR THE PRACTITIONER

Refer to Chapter 7 for a demonstration.

1. Get comfortable and match the person's breathing.

2. Say this to your client: "I am going to help you find a feeling that you still get now, but that originated in your childhood. When you find that feeling, I will touch your shoulder to help you keep that feeling as you travel back in time to your childhood. Is that okay?"

3. Ask for the time and place she feels the undesired feeling.

4. Ask her to go mentally into that time and place now and feel that feeling. Say, "Give me a nod when you have the feeling."

5. After she gives the nod, touch her shoulder to help her hold that feeling.

6. Say, "You've had this feeling many times before. Let this feeling take you all the way back to the first time you had this feeling." Pause and give her time to find it. When she is there, let go of her shoulder.

7. Ask, "Where do you feel the feeling?" Wait for her answer.

8. Ask, "May I touch you there?" Wait for permission.

9. Place your hand there and keep it there until the issue is resolved. You will see physiological shifts such as changes in breathing, skin color, or muscle tension, that let you know the

issue is resolved. Say, "Are we done?" If she says, "Yes," remove your hand. If "No," continue the touch.

10. Say, "Now you can come back to the present."

11. Give her the time to re-orient herself to the present.

12. Ask her to describe the results.

13. Release the bond between yourself and your client.

MELTING A PHYSICAL SYMPTOM

INSTRUCTIONS FOR THE PRACTITIONER

Refer to Chapter 6 for a demonstration.

1. Get comfortable and match the person's breathing.

2. Elicit from your client the physical symptom he wants to dissolve.

3. Ask, "Where in your body is the part that is responsible for this symptom?"

4. Ask, "May I put my hand there?"

5. With permission, place your hand there.

6. Keep your hand there until you feel a shift that lets you believe the process is complete.

7. Ask, "Are we done?" If the answer is "Yes," remove your hand.

8. Be silent while he readjusts to the present.

9. Ask him to describe the results.

10. Release the bond between yourself and your client.

CHANGING A BELIEF

INSTRUCTIONS FOR THE PRACTITIONER

Refer to Chapter 9 for a demonstration.

1. With your client, find the set of limiting beliefs that sur-

round his issue.

2. State the limiting beliefs in his exact words.

3. Write them down. Be sure you get a list of several related beliefs.

4. Get comfortable and match the person's breathing.

5. Ask, "Where do you feel this belief in your body?"

6. Say, "May I touch you there?" Wait for permission.

7. Put your hand there and keep it there until the belief shifts.

8. Ask him to state the new belief.

9. Ask him to state the old belief. He may not be able to state it or he may laugh as he tries to say it.

10. Release the bond between yourself and your client.

DISSOLVING A COMPULSION
INSTRUCTIONS FOR THE PRACTITIONER
Refer to Chapter 4 for a demonstration.

1. Get comfortable and match the person's breathing.

2. Identify the compulsion specifically, what it is, and where and when it occurs.

3. Have the client mentally step into a recent time and place when she felt the compulsion.

4. Ask her to "Let the feeling take you back to the first time you ever had this feeling." This will take her to the generative event, the one that formed the present problem.

5. With permission, place your hand on the location of the feeling and keep it there until the issue is resolved.

6. Bring her up through time from the event to the present, first

A) dissociated, i.e., observing herself from a distance in those contexts, then

B) associated, i.e., seeing out of her own eyes, hearing out of her own ears and feeling her own feelings, going through the same time period. We bring her up through time to change the meaning of a lifetime of experiences. Also, the desired new behavior is more likely to occur if our mind has it coded as if we've always had this behavior and this resource.

7. Invite her to see her future life, first

A) dissociated, seeing herself in the contexts in which the new feelings will be useful, then

B) associated, seeing out of her own eyes, going through the same time period.

We have her specifically go through the problem context in the future because we want to make sure the old cues are associated with the new feelings and behaviors.

8. Release the bond between yourself and your client.

There you have it. A set of processes to heal a multitude of issues. I hope you will use them.

"He that will not apply new remedies must expect new evils; for time is a great innovator."

—Sir Francis Bacon

Finding fulfillment through healing

Chapter Fourteen

What Do You Want?

I'll Help You Get It

Now that you know how to heal others and transform yourself with touch, it's time to explore and decide what benefits you would like to get from it.

If you could have, be or do anything in your life, what would it be? Would you like to:

- Resolve recurring negative emotions?

- Feel more happiness and joy on a daily basis?

- Enjoy your family more?

- Have more rewarding friendships and/or romances?

- Heal painful memories?

- Heal physical pains?

- Transform limiting beliefs?

- Enjoy your work more?

- Open possibilities for the future?

- Write a novel?

- Travel the world?

- Change careers?

- Make a million dollars?

- Get married?

- Improve your athletic performance?

- Improve your musical performance?

- Improve your health?

- Heal others?

- Get a promotion?

- Start a new business?

- Increase your sales?

- Sleep better?

- Be more honest?

- Be more relaxed?

- Be at peace?

- Be connected with spirit?

The possibilities are endless. Only you know which issue you'll find yourself changing first and which ones you'll enjoy changing later. And you'll enjoy discovering which ones will surprise and delight you by changing on their own.

ASK YOURSELF THESE QUESTIONS

1. What is the first change I want to get out of healing with touch?

2. How will I know when I have it? What will I see? What will I hear? What will I feel?

3. When do I want it?

4. When I have what I want from healing with touch, how will that affect my life?

5. How will it affect those around me: friends, family, co-workers?

Repeat steps 1 through 5 as many times as you wish. For ideas, see Chapter 30, Lifelong Healing.

Chapters 14 through 30 help you find issues and give you instructions for healing them.

Your Healing Partner

Although you can do some healing by yourself, I recommend you get a healing partner so that you can heal each other. Your healing partner can help you find your issues, let you relax and focus on your healing, and reach parts of your body that are difficult for you to reach.

Chapter Fifteen

Make Life Easy

If it Feels Good, It's Easier

"I have a hard time with that," you say. What makes something "hard" to do? Most of our activities are not physically taxing for very long. If I carry the washer and dryer up the basement stairs, that is physically hard. But I don't do that very often. I usually work at my computer, or talk with people. So what people often mean when they say things are hard is that they're emotionally hard.

It can be drudgery to take care of a house and kids or to attend to tedious details at work, but if you're feeling good and feeling happy while doing all that, it doesn't seem hard. If you're feeling bad, however, even the most pleasant tasks become heavy burdens.

If we change our emotions, our feelings about what we're doing, then everything gets easier. I like that. I like having everything easier. We have many feelings each day and most of them are the same ones we had the day before. As you know, many of these emotions are not pleasant.

My goal is to transform the feelings from the past, healing emotional injuries that have happened to us, so that we can feel better. I want to get those unpleasant feelings out of the way so that everything will get easier. Let's get our way cleared so we can really GO! Let's be happy, be ecstatic, be excited about where we're going. Let's have life be really worthwhile and fun. This dream becomes reachable with Generative Touch.

The following chapter on emotional chains will give you valuable information on limiting feelings and stuck states you may have in your life. And once you have this information, you can heal and transform them.

Chapter Sixteen

The Child Lies Alone In The Crib...

He gets hungry. He starts to cry. Mother appears. Baby feels excited. Mother nurses baby. Baby feels fulfilled. But Mother is angry. Perhaps she is angry because her husband is not getting up with her to feed the baby. Then Mother feels guilty for feeling angry. Baby picks up the feelings of anger and guilt from the mother. Mother abruptly puts baby down. Baby feels abandoned.

Now we have a chain of emotions: Excited, fulfilled, angry, guilty, and abandoned. If this sequence of events happens several nights in a row, the baby gets programmed with this series of emotions. It's like a record you've heard many times. When one song ends, your mind starts playing the next song before the record does.

This chain then plays itself out over the rest of our lives. In romance, for example. JoAnn feels hungry (for a relationship). She meets Mr. Right and feels excited. She falls in love with Mr. Right and he with her and she feels fulfilled. But the next emotion in her program is anger, so she feels angry, then finds a way to justify the anger, usually by picking on Mr. Right. Her next emotion is guilt, so she feels guilty for picking on him. The sequence repeats until they break up. Then she feels abandoned. She has run the chain from excited to fulfilled to angry to guilty to abandoned.

Another example is planning to go out with friends. Derek feels excited. He goes out and has a good time and feels fulfilled. Then he goes home and finds himself feeling angry, guilty, and abandoned, having no idea why he is having these emotions.

Emotional chains seem to explain how we can have free-floating emotions—feelings that seem to come from nowhere. They can run in several minutes, several hours, or several years, profoundly affecting the quality of everyday life. When I elicit emotional chains, I am often astounded at the frequency and depth of negative emotions people go through day after day, night after night, week after week, month after month, and year after year. Life's many challenges can trigger the chains.

Consider career struggles for example. Here's the string of emotions one man experienced during the sequence of looking for a job, getting the job, working on the job, having problems on the job, and finally leaving the job: apprehension, hopeless-ness, despair, disappointment, disgust, relief, anger, resentment, resignation, apprehension, fear, disorientation, doubt, worthless-ness, disappointment, isolation, defectiveness, unworthiness, doubt, confusion, frustration, contemptuousness, confidence, arrogance, happiness, elation, worthiness, motivation, excite-ment, anticipation, the fullness of possibilities, fulfillment, satis-faction, exhilaration, recognition, stuck, mad, resentment, con-temptuousness, disappointment, pain, sadness, unloved, devalu-ation, worthlessness, slow burn, devaluation, violent anger, dread, stuck, defeat, resignation, resentment, helplessness, con-temptuousness, disconnectedness, sabotage, defeat, gratitude, love, appreciation, worthy, defeat, failure.

Buying a car or a suit can be a harrowing experience. Look at this list of emotions experienced by a woman dealing with a sales person: Excited, disappointed, confused, anxious, torn, wanting, not okay to go for what I want, have to suppress what I want and be nice, a phony type of happy, frustrated, completely alone, sad, confused, anxious, sad, fake happy, angry while also trying to be understanding, worried about the sales person, frustrated, mad at self for not going after what I want, resigned to going for what I want, mad at salesperson, anticipating he'll be mad at me, really angry so I won't back down, guilty, relieved, happy, worried, anxious, angry at self, relieved, a dull nothing, dim hope, disappointed, instant joy, relieved, anxious, worried, suspicious.

Those chains are unusually long. Many chains have five to ten emotions.

Before you say, "But I never have those feelings," consider this:

1) Each person is different. These are the emotional chains of other people, not you. You have your own emotions,

2) The people from whom I elicited these chains didn't know they were having these emotions either. The emotions were mostly in the background, with the person just being aware of being unhappy or unsatisfied,

3) Getting the emotions out where we can "look" at them is one of the tools we need in order to stop these unpleasant chains of emotions and begin feeling better more of the time.

Eliciting and healing emotional chains is already making profound changes in the quality of people's lives by reducing depression, anger, impotence and other symptoms.

You now have the opportunity to think about several experiences in which your emotional chains have operated. You may learn something new about yourself, and you will have a chance to form newer and happier chains.

EMOTIONAL CHAINS

ASK YOURSELF THESE QUESTIONS

What are three occasions such as romances, vacations, or jobs in which I began with positive emotions and ended with negative ones?

As I relive those experiences, what is the sequence of emotions in each?

Now ask your healing partner to help you resolve these feelings using the steps for Resolving an Unpleasant Emotion in Chapter 13.

Chapter Seventeen

The Raging Bull

Is He Out of Control?

Some people have the same negative emotions every day. They're of control, like the bull in the china shop. Feeling hopeless, sad, or anxious, can become a painful, draining, and soul-numbing habit. Fortunately, emotional habits can be changed with touch.

What's your bull doing? Which unpleasant emotions would you prefer to have less frequently? When do you have these emotions? Which emotions would you like to just melt away? Make a list of those emotions. List ten circumstances where you feel each one.

Now ask your healing partner to place her hand where you feel each emotion and keep it there until the emotion dissolves. Do this for each circumstance of each emotion. For full instructions, see Resolving an Unpleasant Emotion in Chapter 13. You may also wish to use the steps for Healing a Painful Memory in the same chapter.

You can check your progress as you heal. Suppose you are working with hopelessness. After you heal hopelessness in one circumstance, ask if the hopelessness is still there for the next circumstance. Say, "When you think of the next circumstance, do you still feel hopeless?" At some point on the list, the answer will be, "No." Usually, when you get a "No" the rest of the circumstances will be healed also. But to make sure, repeat the question for all the remaining circumstances.

Chapter Eighteen

Get A Grip

"My Emotions Made Me Do It!"

Have you ever had the experience of a minor annoyance getting out of control, perhaps turning into rage? Annoyance gets out of control when you get out of your main self and step totally into a raging part. Now, if you get the raging part healed and recombined with your center, you won't get out of control when you get annoyed. There are plenty of things to be annoyed about. I have no problem with being annoyed. But that's different from going into rage every time. Doing rage when the situation is only worth annoyance is hard on you and hard on relationships. And it can lead to violence.

Guilt is another example. Do you ever have guilt that's bigger than the circumstances seem to warrant? This comes from separating—stepping out of yourself and fully into your guilty part. If we heal that part and bring it back in, then you will stay more centered, even when feeling guilt. And you may find yourself seeing things differently, so that you rarely feel guilty. Or you may stop doing things that make you feel guilty.

We have a central core to which most of our parts are connected. As a result of stresses and negative experiences, we have dissociated some of our parts from that core self. And from time to time, we step into one of these dissociated parts. Robert McDonald, a respected NLP trainer, illustrates this point with the "cardboard self" he sometimes used to avoid showing his true self to others. He says he put this cardboard self out in front so that others would look at it—instead of him—so that the real self could stay back where it was safe. This method can help eliminate the need for a cardboard self.

Resolving the emotions is so easy! One of my clients was expecting a promotion at work and was really anxious about it. We spent a few minutes healing the anxiety with touch and she relaxed and got the promotion without stress. Wendy Doran puts it this way: "The negative emotion scrambles. It just...It's gone! It dissolves!"

What prevailing emotions would you like to heal? Fear? Anger? Annoyance? Resentment? Impatience? Guilt? Shame? Sadness? Disgust? Contempt? Helplessness? Hopelessness? Worthlessness? Grief? Despair? Aggressiveness?

ASK YOURSELF THESE QUESTIONS

Are there any emotions I have which I experience more intensely or more often than I would like to? Or, are there any emotions which I experience more intensely than is appropriate or useful for a given situation? When and where do I have these emotions?

Now ask your healing partner to help you resolve these feelings. See Resolving an Unpleasant Emotion in Chapter 13. If you're aware of the events which created these feelings, use Healing a Painful Memory in the same chapter.

In the next three chapters, we give special attention to three emotions: Grief, Fear, and Anger. Grief, because many of us have it and don't know it, so I want to draw your attention to it. Fear, because many of us know we have it, but don't realize how much it influences our lives. And anger, because it is pervasive, it is powerful, and it influences our lives and our health. So I want to be sure you address it fully.

Chapter Nineteen

Grief

How Much Do You Need?

When we lose someone we love through death, divorce, or ending a relationship, the feelings can linger for years. When one loses a limb or an ability through accident or infirmity, the loss can be hard to bear. One can also lose hope. A disappointment in career or education can convince one that there is no use trying; all is lost. Many people wake up one day to find they didn't live the life they expected to. They have lost an expectation. These feelings can be healed. Grieving doesn't have to be a long, drawn-out process. You can heal it quickly with touch.

One client didn't tell me her issue, but as I held my hands on her forearms for a few minutes, tears ran down the sides of her face. When the healing was complete, she said, "After my divorce I had come to believe that my husband had never loved me and no one would ever love me. Now I realize he did love me and I will be loved again."

A seminar participant said, "I was conscious of my hurt and the constant pain from a loss. It was uncanny how you focused on the hurt, really defined it and brought about my healing."

ASK YOURSELF THESE QUESTIONS

What have I lost? What am I grieving about?

Make a list of losses in your life.

Now ask your healing partner to help you resolve these losses with the process for Resolving an Unpleasant Emotion in Chapter 13.

Chapter Twenty

Fear

What Stops You?

Fears can keep you from doing what you want to do. You can have fears of people, places, things, activities, success, or even fear of yourself. Removing these fears can help you be happier and get where you want to go in life. The nice thing about healing fears with touch is that you don't have to know where they came from. You just put your hand where the person feels the fear.

I took a friend boating on a lake in West Virginia. When it came time to get in the water, she said, "I forgot to tell you, I have a water phobia. I can't get in the water." I was a little taken aback that we had gotten this far without her telling me about this fear, but I said, "Would you like to heal your fear with touch?" She said, "Okay" and I put my hand on her forehead where she felt the fear. As I held it there, the fear went away.

She said, "Now I could flip back and swim away like a little guppy!" She went down the boat ladder into the water and paddled away from the boat. With some surprise, I said, "How are you doing? It's 22 feet." She said, "I'm okay. 22 feet. That's a good number."

ASK YOURSELF THESE QUESTIONS

What am I afraid of? What are my fears and phobias?

Now ask your healing partner to help you resolve these fears using Resolving Unpleasant Emotions in Chapter 13.

Chapter Twenty One

Anger

Enough Is Enough!

We carry more anger than any other emotion. Anger is useful. It makes us feel powerful. It is an antidote to our helplessness. I helps us control people. It masks our hurts. It covers our pain. For the numb, it helps us feel. For the guilty, it helps us blame. For the shamed, it helps us regain our self-esteem. It feels familiar and sometimes it feels good. Sometimes it feels comforting.

But it hurts the heart. It fatigues the body. It tires the eyes. It tightens the jaw. It grits the teeth. It cramps the back. It constricts the blood vessels. It raises the blood pressure. It upsets the stomach. It stresses our families. It alienates our co-workers. It causes accidents. It encourages violence. It gives rise to mayhem. It commits murder. It hits the kids. It smokes the cigarettes. It drinks the alcohol. It takes drugs. And sometimes it aims its power at us—with auto-immune disease.

It arises out of repression and pain. From not being allowed to act or express. From abuse, punishment, shame, neglect, trauma, and torture.

Anger serves us well. When we have nothing better, it's a powerful drug. It makes us feel strong. Or self-righteous. But like any other drug, it's habit-forming. It's addictive. So it may take longer to resolve your anger than any other emotion. Here's what I want you to do:

1. Every day, make a list of what you are angry about.

2. As often as you can, get your healing partner to heal your angers.

3. Do this until you can't find any anger to put on your list.

Chapter Twenty Two

Aches And Pains

What Do They Want?

Pain is a message from the unconscious mind. When we respond to the message, the pain often stops. Sometimes the body doesn't know the war is over. It just needs to know it is safe. Or it needs to know that pain is a natural part of healing. In many cases, the cause of the pain is long forgotten; we don't know what the pain is about. With Generative Touch, we don't have to know what's causing the pain; we just treat it directly with touch.

Pain in one of my cancer patients came partly from a tumor and partly from fear. When we reduced her fear, the pain reduced also. Another client felt anger in her arm because there was someone she needed to punch. After a session with touch, her tendinitis went away for a month.

In Chapter 6, Bill found new realizations as he healed pains in his back and stomach. Bill's pain seemed to be from stress. Pain can also be caused by a slipped disc, tissue degeneration, or other physical causes. Generative Touch is useful in reducing these pains, but if you do plenty of touch and the pain continues, encourage your client to see a doctor.

Sometimes the client will come to you already knowing the

physical cause of the pain: a broken bone (which has already been set, I hope), a tumor, or a sprain, for example. Generative Touch can greatly reduce that type of pain. Just remember: you're not responsible for removing all physical pain, no matter what is causing it. In addition to your touch, medical treatment may be in order. Even so, the pain can usually be reduced and the patient may get useful insights. I wonder what you will discover as you heal your aches and pains.

The woman in chapter one with the knots in her back had pain that was first caused by physical trauma, an auto accident. The lingering pain, however, was caused by habit. Part of her didn't know the threat had passed. When we let that part feel safe, the pain stopped.

The mind-body connection can cause physical symptoms other than pain, so I encourage you to try touch with any symptom. I've had good results with the bloating, swelling, and tenderness that occur with PMS, for example.

ASK YOURSELF THESE QUESTIONS

What physical symptoms do I have, including aches and pains, high blood pressure, etc. ?

When did each symptom begin?

Now ask your healing partner to assist your healing with Melting Away Physical Symptoms in Chapter 13.

Some of the symptoms may have begun after a traumatic event. If you know what the event was, use the steps for Healing a Painful Memory in Chapter 13.

Chapter Twenty Three

How's Your Health?

Can Touch Improve It?

Drug abuse, obesity, cancer, heart disease, smoking—why not tackle these with Generative Touch? A mountain of research points to the connection between emotions and disease. Emotions are not responsible for all disease, but medical research indicates that emotional balance and well-being can support healing and aid in the prevention of diseases of many kinds.

The immune system may be the link between emotions and infectious disease, auto-immune disease, allergies, and cancer, a link which cancer researchers have examined. Cancer accounts for 23% of all deaths in the United States and deaths due to cancer have risen 20% in the past 30 years, according to the American Cancer Society. Therefore, a great deal of money flows into cancer research and some of that money has been used to examine the link between emotions and disease.

Cancer researchers have concluded that psychological stress weakens the immune system.[1] According to Barbara L. Anderson, Janice K. Kiecolt-Glaser, and Ronald Glaser, researchers at the Ohio State University, "Stress-associated changes in immune function occur as a result of the physiological changes that take place (i.e. alterations in levels of hormones and neuropeptides). These changes ultimately affect different aspects of immune function."[2]

Therapy to reduce stress has been found to extend the lives of cancer patients. David Spiegel and other researchers at Stanford University performed a 10-year study of the effect of group therapy on cancer patients. They found that patients with metastatic breast cancer who attended weekly group therapy for one year lived, on average, twice as long as a control group who did not attend meetings. The group program focused on "living as fully as possible, improving communication with family members and doctors, facing and mastering fears about death and dying, and controlling pain and other symptoms."[3] This lets us know that emotions and beliefs affect life span.

As early as 1980, O. Carl Simonton, MD., et al., reported that patients who received psychological intervention "survived up to twice as long as would have been expected based on national averages." In his article Psychological Intervention in the Treatment of Cancer, he said, "Emotional responses that have been reported to correlate with an undesirable course of malignancy include depression, denial, repression, regression, defensiveness, and rigidity of beliefs. Characteristics that appear to correlate with unusually good disease courses are emotional resiliency, physical activity, flexibility of beliefs, strong self-concept, and social autonomy."[4] More evidence that emotions influence health.

Auto-immune diseases result from a confused, angry, or dejected immune system attacking the body. It is possible that when emotional issues are healed, the immune system will resume its role of protecting you.

Allergies result from the immune system treating a manageable substance as if it were a life-threatening one.

There are over a hundred years of research linking disease to stress and trauma. We have compelling evidence that healing our emotions can strengthen the immune system, support medical treatment, and lead to better health.

The questions in this section are designed to help you discover which emotions are affecting your life in a negative direction. When you find those emotions and heal them, your health may improve.

Chapter Twenty Four

Friendships

Make Them Better

If friendships don't last, or if they have more conflict in them you'd like, your emotions may be the cause.

If, on the other hand, you avoid friendships, you may be dodging hurts like you experienced in the past. When you resolve the emotions, friendships get better.

ASK YOURSELF THESE QUESTIONS

What are my three biggest failures, regrets, or bad feelings concerning friendships?

As I look at these three, what looks, sounds, or feels the same about all three?

When I think about these feelings, has either of my parents or a former friend or partner ever made me feel that way? If so, who?

What types of situations with this person made me feel that way?

What physical sensations do I have in my body when I think of those situations?

Now ask your healing partner to help you resolve these feelings using Chapter 13, steps for Resolving an Unpleasant Emotion.

Chapter Twenty Five

Relationships

Really? How?

Relationships require love, safety, consistency, honesty, and trust. If your relationships blow up or just dwindle, or if you drop him/her before he/she drops you, or if they end and you're at a complete loss as to why, then healing emotions around them may remove obstacles and lead to longer-lasting, happier relationships.

ASK YOURSELF THESE QUESTIONS

What are my three biggest failures, regrets, or bad feelings concerning relationships?

As I look at these three, what looks, sounds, or feels the same about all three?

When I think about these feelings, has either of my parents or a former friend or partner ever made me feel that way? If so, who?

What types of situations with this person made me feel that way?

What physical sensations do I have in my body when I think of those situations?

Now ask your healing partner to help you resolve these feelings using the steps for Resolving an Unpleasant Emotion in Chapter 13.

Chapter Twenty Six

Family

The Challenge Court

The family can be the toughest environment in which to talk things out. You try to talk, and they come back with the same old stuff and you're yelling or fighting or withdrawing again.

After you heal your emotional wounds, you won't be so likely to take the bait. You'll be able to forgive yourself and others and to recover your boundaries and your self respect. Your need to be aggressive will be reduced or eliminated.

In chapter one I talked about a client whose mother had forced her to have a nose job. She was angry with her mother for many years. By healing her own feelings around the issue, she was able to forgive her mother. At the same time, she was able to set clearer boundaries with regard to her body.

ASK YOURSELF THESE QUESTIONS

What are my three biggest failures, regrets, or bad feelings concerning my family?

As I look at these three, what looks, sounds, or feels the same about all three?

When I think about these feelings, has either of my parents

or a former friend or partner ever made me feel that way? If so, who?

What types of situations with this person made me feel that way?

What physical sensations do I have in my body when I think of those situations?

Now ask your healing partner to help you resolve these feelings using the steps for Resolving an Unpleasant Emotion in Chapter 13.

Chapter Twenty Seven

Work

How To Impress Your Boss Without Really Trying

The workplace can be toxic to your mental health. One of my clients thought he was having a heart attack, but when he went to the hospital, he learned it was stress. We healed his anxiety with touch, and now he's enjoying his work.

If you're enjoying your work less than you would like to, this process will help you make a quantum leap in finding fulfillment. And when you're more fulfilled, your performance will skyrocket.

ASK YOURSELF THESE QUESTIONS

What are my three biggest failures, regrets, or bad feelings about jobs, tasks, or my career in general?

As I look at these three, what looks, sounds, or feels the same about all three?

When I think about these feelings, has either of my parents or a former friend or partner ever made me feel that way? Has a former boss, co-worker, supervisor, customer, supplier, or employee ever made me feel that way? If so, who?

What types of situations with this person made me feel that way?

What physical sensations do I have in my body when I think of those situations?

Now ask your healing partner to use Resolving an Unpleasant Emotion in Chapter 13 to help you resolve these feelings.

Chapter Twenty Eight

Success

Do Beliefs Make a Difference?

Some years ago I saw a film showing a pike fish in an aquarium with guppies. The pike is very strong and fast, able to nip off guppies at will. Then a glass cylinder is lowered vertically into the tank and the guppies are all placed inside it. Pike can't see the cylinder because it becomes invisible when immersed in the water. So each time the pike strikes at a guppy, its nose slams painfully into the cylinder. After a few hundred unsuccessful attempts and a severely battered nose, the pike gives up. It has learned to believe it cannot get to the guppies.

Then the cylinder is removed and the guppies swim free. But the pike doesn't strike at them. The pike is given no other food, yet it starves to death before trying to strike a guppy.

Beliefs are what we experience as truth. Our deepest ones are so automatic and unconscious that we usually don't know we have them. Some are installed with the voices of others. Some are gained from experience. It is estimated that parents say no to a child 15,000 times. I wonder how many negative beliefs that installs.

Typically we're aware of four types of beliefs:
- Religious beliefs
- Beliefs we are trying to hold on to
- Beliefs we have recently changed
- Beliefs we are trying to change

We usually want to keep our religious beliefs, but we may have some others that we'd like to change because we realize they are holding us back or making us feel bad. How to change beliefs?

Some people try to use affirmations to change beliefs. They repeat, "I'm a happy and successful person." a hundred times a day. But the old belief, adopted long ago, may be saying, "I can't do anything right. I'm a failure." The old belief will fight the new one, causing stress. The way to get a new belief is to dissolve the old one by healing the negative emotions that are part of it, creating space for a new one.

Unsuccessful people tend to have beliefs like:

I have to,

I can't,

I must,

I should,

There's no way,

It's impossible, or similar limiting words.

Highly successful people tend to have beliefs that are more useful. The successful person will have beliefs more like,

I want to,

I can,

There is a way,

It's possible for me,

There is an opportunity here, and similar action-oriented beliefs.

Until recently, many people thought they were stuck with their limiting beliefs, or they tried to change them by brute force. Now we know it is possible, and even easy, to use touch to gently change the beliefs that hold us back. But first, we need to unearth those limiting beliefs.

ASK YOURSELF THESE QUESTIONS

What stops me from doing, being, or having everything I want? Is it age, health, race, identity, feelings of unworthiness or of not being deserving, other people, self-control, capabilities, longevity, relationships, habits, addictions, what is possible or impossible, money, or something else?

Whatever stops you, write it down. Make it into a sentence. For example, if you think age is stopping you, put "age" into a sentence. The sentence could be, "I can't start a new business at my age." That sentence is a limiting belief. Write a limiting belief sentence for each thing that is stopping you from having what you want.

Now ask your healing partner to help you resolve these limiting beliefs using Changing A Belief in Chapter 13.

Chapter Twenty Nine

Healing Yourself

Try It, You'll Like It!

Most of the cases in this book assume you will be healing someone else or they will be healing you. If you don't have anyone to work with, however, it is possible to heal yourself. While most of the examples in this book are about one person healing another, Robin talks about healing herself in Chapter 7 and Leslie talks about it this chapter.

Each method has its advantages. You are always available to heal yourself, so you can get help when no one else is around. Receiving healing from others has several advantages, though. First, it's easier for someone else to keep their hand on your body than it is for you. This is especially important if the healing takes more than a few minutes. Secondly, another person can help you find what you need to heal. And third, you can relax and focus on your healing.

So, when you have someone to heal you, take advantage of the opportunity. When you don't have someone, heal yourself. When I sprained my ankle recently, friends did most of the healing for me, holding their hands on my ankle for 45 minutes at a time. That would have been hard to do by myself, considering the position I have to get into to hold my ankle. When my friends weren't available, I did some healing by myself, holding my ankle for brief periods.

When I recently had a very intense emotional issue that I felt in my eyes, a friend helped me heal much of it. When more came up later, I just placed the palms of my hands on my eyes and kept them there for several minutes. The issue continued to resolve.

Here's what my editor said about healing herself:

"When an editor works on a manuscript, she expects to change it, but she doesn't expect to be changed by it. Editing *Generative Touch*, however, has been a unique experience for me.

"As I read the manuscript, I felt excited by the possibilities of Generative Touch, yet skeptical that something so simple could do so much. So I began to place my hands on myself in the way John described.

"The results were remarkable. In the weight room, I strained my neck while bending down to pick up a weight. I placed my hand on my neck and the pain was gone in five minutes. After being shamed by someone, I put my hand on my chest and felt a powerful feeling of confidence and self-love. And whenever I felt too scattered to work on the manuscript, I would place my hands where the feeling originated. In two minutes, I would be ready to work. I was able to make these changes even though I had no background in healing with my hands and no previous exposure to John's method—just by reading this book."

—Leslie Kaufman Viktora

Chapter Thirty

Lifelong Healing

For The Part Of You That Wants It All

If you want to heal even more, review the list below. It's a shopping mall of issues to heal. You can heal issues about the present, the past, and the future for yourself and others. By using this list, you may find issues you didn't realize you had; issues that, although subtle, when resolved will make your life more comfortable.

You may be surprised at the length of the list. The possibility of healing all these issues with one method sounds amazing, doesn't it? It is amazing. I'm amazed, too. But this is a new concept. And with new concepts come new possibilities. So open your mind.

ASK THESE QUESTIONS
The Present

Do you put things off? Are you waiting a few more days before you begin to write that book, change your career, apologize to your friend, quit smoking, clean up your desk, do your laundry, wash your car, write your résumé, heal yourself, or start your new business?

Are you late for meetings and appointments? Have you tried

to be on time, but find yourself still being late?

Are you forgetful? Do you forget commitments, your keys, your appointments, your grocery list? Do you forget what you were going to say? Do you forget what you learned for the test?

Do you hesitate to ask for what you want? Do you avoid asking for the order, a job, a promotion, a raise, a price, a favor, a date, a kiss, or a hug? Is it hard for you to ask directions when you're lost, a price in a store, or permission to be included in a meeting or group?

Is it difficult for you to maintain healthy relationships? Do they tend to blow up? Do you connect with the wrong type of person? Are you too dominant or submissive? Too intrusive or distant? Or have you been avoiding relationships entirely?

Do you try to control others? Do you insist on having it your way and feel frustrated when you don't?

Do you hesitate to apologize? Or confront? Do you avoid resolving smoldering issues? At home, at work, with the kids, with your parents, with your siblings, with your friends, or with stores?

Are you confused about what to do? Or how to feel? Are you pulled in opposite directions? Do you have feelings in conflict?

Are you in pain? From injuries? From surgery? From emotional wounds?

Are you wondering why you still hurt? Are you searching for wholeness and well-being?

Are you starved for touch? Would you like to have a safe, non-sexual, healing touch that feeds your skin's need for contact?

Are you in emotional pain? Do you have anxiety, anger, resentment, fear, sadness, guilt, shame, hate, rage, blame, phobias, remorse, or hypervigilance?

Do you throw tantrums? Does it upset those around you?

Does it threaten your job or security?

Are you too aggressive? Or violent?

Are you unable to have satisfying sex? Are you unable to feel? Unable to enjoy? Unable to perform?

Have you been getting sick? Does your mind make you sick? Have you experienced emotions taking their toll on your body with knots in your stomach, indigestion, gas, colitis, chest pain, headaches, migraines, stiff joints, high blood pressure, hair loss, cramps, weakness, fatigue, sore muscles, or feeling tired and achy?

Is everything everybody else's fault?

Do you hate yourself? Or parts of yourself? Are you feeling self-hate because of what you are doing to yourself or because of what was done to you?

Do you have unpleasant habits? Or dangerous ones? Do you eat too much? Drink too much? Smoke too much? Take too many risks? Gamble with your life or your money?

Are you still angry at someone who is not in your life anymore? Perhaps even someone who is dead?

Are you depressed? Have you lost your pictures of the future? Are most of your thoughts negative? Do you repress anger and rage? Do you keep playing old memories over in your mind? Are you becoming detached, bitter, lonely, or despondent?

Do you have nightmares? Do you want them to end? What would it be like to end them now?

Does your child have nightmares? Are you tired of being wakened up in the middle of the night? Are you worried about the pain your child is suffering?

Are you numb? Have you lost part of your ability to feel your emotions or your body? Do you feel you're missing something? Do you wonder what people mean when they talk about feelings?

Do you feel other people owe you or should take care of you?

The Past

Were you abused or neglected as a child or adult? Perhaps by someone you loved or trusted? Is the pain of those memories still with you? Do you have tension, fear, hypervigilance, inability to trust, or the feeling that your world may come crashing down around you at any moment? Are you unable to set boundaries, know what you want, or moderate your behavior?

Have you experienced the trauma of war, terrorism, surgery, or other violence? Does the trauma still haunt you? Are you continuing to feel the pain, the anxiety, and the fear?

Have you wasted lots of time and money trying to be healed? Have you been to therapy which left you in as much pain as before you started?

Were you a late bloomer? Did you graduate late? Marry late? Have children late? Make money late? Have you been criticized for it? Do you criticize yourself for it?

The Future

Do you want to remove obstacles to success? Is something stopping you from succeeding? Do you make excuses? Do you find yourself doing anything but what it would take to make you rich and famous or happy and serene?

Do you have anxiety? Are you anxious about a meeting or speech? About your spouse coming home from work? About a promotion? About someone learning your secret? Going on vacation? Moving to a new home?

Are you on edge about upcoming surgery, chemotherapy, or other medical treatment? Do you fear medical examinations? Are you afraid of going to the dentist?

Do you feel like giving up? Does it get to be too much sometimes? Do you feel like you'll never have what you want?

Are you afraid to feel? Are feelings scary for you? Does it seem dangerous to feel? Would you like to have a safe and gentle way to re-connect with your feelings?

Do you want to avoid the "family disease"? Are you concerned because cancer, heart attack, arthritis, alcoholism, or other diseases have been in your family?

Do you want to avoid cancer? Do you want to heal life experiences linked with cancer? In his book, Cancer, Illness Of The Soul, Dr. Ryke Hamer explains how cancer is often triggered by trauma. He says resolving the trauma can heal the cancer. Other authors attribute recovery from cancer to resolving losses, expressing emotions, enjoying life, keeping a coherent view of the world, having a desired future, and having a purpose for living.

Is your life going nowhere? Do you believe you could do more with your life, but something stops you? And you don't know what it is?

Are your beliefs holding you back? Do you have negative beliefs about yourself, the world, and other people—beliefs that keep you from reaching your potential?

Are you afraid of failing? Do you fear embarrassment, criticism, ridicule, or self punishment?

Are you afraid of having what you want? Do you fear that your life would change in ways you don't want it to?

* * *

It can be this way, but it doesn't have to. You can change it.

Afterword

When you started this book, if I had promised you that you could become an amazing healer, you might have been skeptical. But now I can tell you: You can become an amazing healer. You have learned the secrets and skills that can make you a powerful healer. You can heal emotional wounds, painful memories, and physical pain. You can even change limiting beliefs to ones of empowerment and passion. *Generative Touch* was written to demystify the art of healing. Now that you've learned the simple concepts, techniques, and attitudes presented here, you know:

1. What you can heal
2. How to prepare for healing
3. When, where, and how to touch
4. How to know you're healing
5. When and how to release the touch

You can heal physical, mental, emotional and spiritual issues very quickly. Healing and transformation often come in less than ten minutes, and usually in less than an hour.

Your ability to heal with this method is not limited by what you're doing now or what you've done in the past. Your career and your education are irrelevant to this process. It's your humanness that enables you to heal.

The method presented here not only heals safely and quickly; it heals a vast range of personal issues. Of course I didn't know that at first, so when the healings began, I was excited, but I was also skeptical. Was it really healing? Would the results last? Only time and experience could answer. And they have. By now, I've healed with Generative Touch hundreds of times. I've been healing for several years. And my clients, including the very first one, tell me their changes have stayed with them. People who have learned to heal this way by attending my seminars, reading this book, or being my client, have reported wonderful successes also. So I became convinced. I think you will, too.

I would like to thank many people who have assisted me in bringing this book into being. Thanks to Pat Baker who told me I have healing hands. Special thanks to my early clients who so generously let me test my new ideas with them. Tamara Andreas encouraged me to continue developing and using the process. I thank my many teachers, including Bill and Dean McGrane, Gerry Schmidt, Charles Faulkner, Tom Best, Tim Hallbom, Suzi Smith, Connirae, Steve, and Tamara Andreas, Michael Banks, Robert Dilts, Art Giser, John Friedlander, Lara Ewing, Robert McDonald, Kelly Gerling, Gary Faris, and John Grinder.

David Calof provided ideas on how parts are formed and Tim McPike explained primal chains and provided ideas on enriching one's work, relationships, friendships and family life. Robert McDonald pointed out that feelings have a location in the body. Tom Best provided the true story of Gus.

Dr. Barry Bates provided scientific data on the relationships between stress, immune response, and cancer. John Grinder presented the hummingbird metaphor. Chris Thompson insisted

I write the book. Michael Zakarian's beautiful cover artwork and typography inspired me to get this book done. My editor, Leslie Kaufman Viktora, encouraged me, helped me learn to write and edit, and helped to shape the book. The book has seen many revisions since Leslie last saw it, though, so any remaining errors are mine.

I also want to thank the people at Writer's Digest in Cincinnati, Ohio. During the latest two years of writing, I have been reading this magazine each month, and it has given me ideas, encouragement, skills, and hope.

Siegrid Bown translated the book into German, took it to Germany, and brought back feedback and suggestions. Craig White transcribed the seminar tapes. Mel Hensey, Helen Parmater, Sue Catana, Sherry Keener, Steve Andreas, Stephanie Woolcot, and Ray Hoskins reviewed the manuscript and gave valuable feedback.

Thanks to my seminar participants who so enthusiastically reported their results. And I thank my kids: Eric for being my continuous friend and supporter and Matthew and Susan for believing in me no matter what I do.

And, finally, thank you for wanting to heal.

Generative Touch is a specific method of giving mental, physical, emotional, and spiritual support to the one being healed. It provides a conceptual framework and a clear procedure that allows almost anyone to heal consistently and successfully.

I hope you will use Generative Touch to heal yourself, your friends, and your loved ones. If you are a health practitioner, you can use it to support your present methods of healing. I believe this way of healing with touch is the breakthrough method we can use to heal the planet.

Footnotes

Chapter 3

1. Shreeve, James, (1993) Touching The Phantom. *Discover* pp. 35-42. The article says: Neuroscientist Vilayanur Ramachandran, head of the Brain and Perception Laboratory at the University of California at San Diego, has done research regarding "phantom limbs," the perception of vivid feelings that seemingly come from the missing limbs of amputees. It had been believed that severed nerve endings were sending impulses to the brain, giving an amputee the same feeling as if the arm or leg were still attached. Doctors attempted to relieve the pain by clipping the ends of the severed nerves. However, trimming the nerve endings provided only temporary relief. By cutting the nerves closer and closer to the brain and finding that the pain always came back, Ramachandran concluded that the true seat of the sensation of touch lies not in the skin or in the nerves, but within the brain itself.

Neurobiologists Gary Duncan and Catherine Bushnell of the University of Montreal used positron emission tomography scans and magnetic resonance images of the brain to indicate areas stimulated by pain. They found that the front portion of the cingulate gyrus, the brain's emotional headquarters, is very active during painful stimulation. Painful experiences create emotional records in the brain.

Chapter 23

1. Anderson, B. L., Kiecolt-Glaser, J.K., Glaser, R., (1994) A Biobehavioral Model of Cancer Stress and Disease Course. *American Psychologist,* 49. 389-404.

O'Leary. A. (1990) Stress, emotion, and human immune function. *Psychological Bulletin,* 108, 363-382.

Herbert, T.B., & Cohen, S. (1993a). Depression and immunity: A meta-analytic review. *Psychological bulletin* 113, 472-486.

Herbert, T.B., & Cohen, S. (1993b). Stress and immunity in humans: A meta-analytic review. *Psychosomatic Medicine,* 55. 364-379.

2. Kiecolt-Glaser, J.K., Glaser, R., (1988). Psychological influences on immunity: Implications for AIDS. *American Psychologist,* 43. 892-898.

3. Spiegel, D., Bloom, J.R., Kraemer, H.C., & Gottheil, E. (1989, October 14). Effect of psycho-social treatment on survival of patients with metastatic breast cancer. *Lancet,* pp. 888-891.

4. O. Carl Simonton, Stephanie Matthews-Simonton, T. Flint Sparks (1980). Psychological intervention in the treatment of cancer. *Psychosomatics,* 21: 226-233.

~FUTURE LEARNING~

An audiotape set and live seminars on Generative Touch are available. Call 800-229-4657 or write to the publisher for information.

~ABOUT THE AUTHOR~

John Parmater is a researcher, teacher, inventor, and father of three. He has helped hundreds of people to heal and transform their lives, successfully resolving issues ranging from compulsions to physical and sexual abuse, physical pain, sexual dysfunction, phobias, cancer, arthritis, relationship problems, lack of motivation, negative feelings, nightmares, flashbacks, confusion, lack of direction, alcoholism, migraine headaches, and more. He has been facilitating healing with Generative Touch since 1990.

Before entering the healing profession, John was a research engineer, marketer, and business planner, he co–invented a mass spectrometer, an auto computer, and the bill dispenser for an automatic teller. Now he applies his creative ability to developing methods for healing.

He is distressed to see people in so much pain and he wants to help end useless suffering. So he teaches people to heal. John wants to train many people to do the process, so that when he is no longer on the earth, the healing will continue. He hopes you will join him and become part of this major healing of the planet.

John is co-director of Bodymind Center, Inc., a treatment center with the goal of extending the lives of people with life-threatening disease, and co-director of NLP of Ohio, Inc., a training center for Neuro-linguistic Programming (NLP). John maintains a private practice in Columbus, Ohio, and trains Generative Touch and NLP.